USING PSYCHOSOCIAL COUNSELLING TECHNIQUES IN PRIMARY HEALTH CARE

*For our mothers
whose influence appears on each page*

Using Psychosocial Counselling Techniques in Primary Health Care

ELLEN JESPERSEN
P. F. PEGG

Avebury

Aldershot · Brookfield USA · Hong Kong · Singapore · Sydney

Published by
Avebury
Gower Publishing Company Limited
Gower House, Croft Road
Aldershot, Hants GU11 3HR
England

Gower Publishing Company
Old Post Road
Brookfield, Vermont 05036
USA

British Library Cataloguing in Publication Data

Jespersen, Ellen
　　Using psychosocial counselling techniques
　in primary health care.
　　1. Family psychotherapy　2. Psychotherapy,
　Brief
　　I. Title　　II. Pegg, Patricia F.
　　616.89'156　　　　RC488.5

Library of Congress Cataloging-in-Publication Data

Jespersen, Ellen, 1929–
　　Using psychosocial counselling techniques
in primary health care.
　　Bibliography: p.
　　Includes index.
　　1. Psychotherapy, Brief — Case studies.
2. Family medicine.　I. Pegg, Patricia F.　II. Title.
RC480.55.J47　　1987　　610　　87-8784

ISBN　0 566 05463 9

Printed and bound in Great Britain by
Biddles Limited, Guildford and King's Lynn

Contents

Acknowledgements

Using Psychosocial Counselling Techniques in Primary Health Care is about quite ordinary people. In the case studies they appear special. This is not because they followed their doctors' advice and went to a family or brief therapist, but because the stories of most all ordinary people are inherently interesting — in some respect 'special'. To these patients and their doctors we want to express our thanks. Their common confidence created the basis for this book. Their stories are real, though names, sex and other identifying characteristics have been changed to prevent recognition.

In Dr Tony Manocchio, who once long ago brought us together, we have had a creative and inspiring teacher. Tony's encouragement, provocation and faith in our ability cannot be overestimated.

On its way to publication the book or parts of it has been read by several people, whose opinions, criticism and advice have been of great help to us. We are indebted to Donald A. Block, Florence Bruell, Helen Roberts and Carlos E. Sluski. Hugo Freeman and Przemek Bogdanowich read the manuscript and made helpful comments about the text. We accept full responsibility for the way we used all feedback.

The fundamental message of the book is quite simple. We want to thank Jane Anthony, our editor at Gower, for recognizing the significance of this message and for creating the opportunity for a wide audience to learn from it.

Ellen Jespersen   P.F. Pegg
December 1986

Foreword
M. SALKIND

Those of us who work in general practice are conscious of our role in detecting, classifying and treating organic disease. It has long been recognized that this approach has fossilized in many medical schools as a direct and continuing consequence of the changes made by Flexner, and his emphasis on the scientific as opposed to the philosophical and mythical attitude to illness. This set of attitudes has been compounded by the technological revolution of the past quarter of a century, which has seen changes almost equal to all that existed previously in scientific knowledge. Small wonder then that patients who have problems turn to the 'scientific world', embodied for them in scientific medicine, with the profound feeling that if there is malfunction it must necessarily be due to a faulty part, cf. an automobile, and must be amenable to treatment. 'If a part is wrong, cut it out, replace it, or change it by chemicals.' The net, and inevitable consequence is a reliance upon the world of medicine. Even more, since health is now sanctified as an essential prerogative, a positive rather than a negative possession, the absence of health promotes a demand for restitution of a natural right. What we now see is a progressive and remorseless progression towards a reliance on medicine and its hierarchical systems, the essential ingredient of which is the eventual surrender of the autonomy of the patient.

Using Psychosocial Counselling Techniques in Primary Health Care is about the restitution of this autonomy and is founded, like the location of its work, on the fundamental belief that human beings want to be responsible, either to themselves or to the communities; and also that people contain within themselves all possibilities including the possibility to be healthy or healthier. Whilst this is clearly an oversimplification it initiates progress towards restoring self-help, self-respect, personal autonomy and growth.

There is embodied in the text the idea that the patients' view of themselves is critical, and that the problems presented are the results of mishandled difficulties. This is not new, nor are the processes by which the patients' vision is clarified. What does emerge is that many major problems that impinge upon and may ultimately destroy the basic health of an individual may be resolved by skilful handling resulting in relatively minor but effective adjustments by the patients themselves. This is of course deceptively simple to achieve, but our authors demonstrate what is possible in practice without recourse to the more intensive psychotherapeutic regimens, and represents a fundamental recognition of the relationship between the individual and his whole environment. It sets out the thesis that traditional medical diagnosis cannot and should not impose its own limits on the improvement of the health of any patient.

Professor M.R. Salkind
Professor of General Practice and Primary Care

Joint Department of General Practice and Primary Care, the Medical Colleges of St Bartholomew's and the London Hospital, London

January 1987

1 Psychosocial Counselling in Context

This book is about how psychosocial counselling methods — mainly those of brief therapy — have been integrated into the treatment programme of a primary health care practice in a community in Denmark. The book has two aims. Firstly, it seeks to demonstrate how psychosocial counselling can make a significant contribution to patient care.

Translating knowledge into useful action in face-to-face contacts with patients or clients is a ubiquitous problem. Many general practitioners regard dealing with psychosocial factors to be one of the most difficult and frustrating professional problems they encounter (Beitman *et al.* 1982; Brockway 1978; Friedman *et al.* 1978a,b,c,d). The book addresses the issue of applying psychosocial knowledge and methods in work with patients, by describing different ways in which the brief therapy model has been employed, and explaining the rationale behind its use.

Judging the usefulness or appropriateness of psychotherapeutic intervention also poses problems for many practitioners (Adams and Hill 1983; Jordan 1981; Watzlawick *et al.* 1977). This seems to be a particular issue for those who work in general settings. By general setting, we mean institutions or agencies whose function is to meet and assist a broad range of patients or clients — basically, whoever comes through the door. So while specifically written within the context of a general medical practice, it is intended that the book can be of use to social workers, community workers, teachers, nurses, clerical personnel and mental health workers who meet a broad range of client needs in their work.

Secondly, the book aims to illustrate some of the benefits for patients of receiving brief psychotherapeutic intervention. The provision of psychosocial counselling in a primary health care clinic means that professional assistance is readily available to persons who might not ordinarily seek it. The opportunity this affords is important. While evidence links life events with somatic, economic, psychological and social well-being, it is clear that most people undergoing difficult times do not ordinarily seek counselling or other professional assistance (see for example, Parkes 1981). They do go to their doctors.

A psychotherapeutic perspective offered to patients in a setting with which they are familiar can help them to recognize that some of the elements of a physical symptom or problem can be positively altered through means within their own range or control. This can be seen in Robert's story, in Chapter 3. His symptoms lead to the opportunity for him to evaluate how his ways of relating to the environment provoked his somatic condition, and to discover ways in which he might realistically improve the quality of his general health, and of his life (Fisch *et al.* 1982; Kubler-Ross 1969; Lewis *et al.* 1976; Metze 1981; Schneider 1981; Simonton and Simonton 1978; Zorn 1982).

This chapter introduces the book and Laegernes Hus, the primary health care centre, in Denmark. In Chapter 2 the brief therapy model will be described in detail. Patient cases are presented in story format, rather than as case analyses or in sessional transcript form. The stories are intended to demonstrate how the brief therapy model is put into practice. Hopefully, they will stimulate the reader to re-examine his or her views about what is significant, useful and effective in treatment. The story format locates psychotherapy or professional intervention in due perspective: as one aspect in the life of the patient. This contrasts with a style of presentation which emphasizes a therapist's methodology as the most interesting or important part of the patient.

Patients come to their doctors at Laegernes Hus with medical complaints, psychiatric disorders, and behavioural and generalized distress symptoms. The expectation when a patient puts forth a problem is that his doctor will act in some way that either cures the symptom, solves the problem, or increases possible ways of dealing with the complaint or its consequences. Patients generally expect to receive some form of intervention to alleviate the symptom, or to alter the problem state: a medical prescription, advice, prescribed ritual behaviour, or, occasionally, by requesting certification of certain physical conditions, indirect financial assistance (Kleinman 1980).

The book aims to address the problems of introducing brief psychotherapy to patients who come to the doctor with a medical rather than psychological or social problem. Brief therapy was the model of psychotherapeutic treatment used at Laegernes Hus with individuals or families at a time in their lives when they were motivated either to manage their symptoms or problems in another way, or to find a new solution for them. Often an outsider's appreciation of their ability to cope with difficult circumstances, or the assurance that their behaviour is quite normal, sufficed. Petra's story is one example of this, but there are a number throughout the book.

To say that they were motivated does not mean that these patients explicitly requested psychotherapy. Some of the patients received conventional medical treatment for long periods, then 'suddenly' requested special help, as can be seen in Jenny's story in the following chapter. Others, because of special events — divorce, abortion, unemployment

2

or overemployment, death of a loved one — or as a consequence of ordinary life transitions — sought new ways to deal with their circumstances. Sometimes this meant learning new techniques for dealing with people around them (Bohannan 1971; Haley 1976; Krantzler 1975; Madanes 1981; Parkes 1972 and 1981; Schoenberg *et al.* 1970; Watzlawick *et al.* 1974; Weakland *et al.* 1974; Weiss 1973 and 1975). This book describes some of the symptoms which patients brought to Laegernes Hus, identifies problem areas, highlights the social forces involved, and demonstrates a therapeutic approach which brings about positive change.

The majority of patients at Laegernes Hus, as at most general practices, manage adequately in the community. They may be assisted by kin, social service supports, or by prescribed medication, but they maintain in some form their jobs, social contacts, and family lives (Gottlieb 1981). Where a symptom threatens a patient's physiological or social condition, a timely and appropriate intervention can avert progression to a grave medical or psychiatric state. But the patients are not formally obliged to receive psychotherapeutic treatment. The non-compulsory nature of therapy in this open care setting — as opposed to conditions linked with imperative social welfare, probationary supervision, and the like — influences the psychosocial treatment model employed. Most patients retain sufficient coping mechanisms at the point when they visit their GP to exercise selection. If they do not experience some value in the treatment, or if they feel blamed for a situation in which they already feel helpless, they shift to another adapting mode. Then the therapist has failed (Fisch *et al.* 1982; Haley 1976).

The brief therapy model described does not constitute the form of treatment offered to all patients. Management of somatic symptoms, and the percentage of patients who actually received brief therapy are discussed later in this introduction. The factors which signalled or suggested the advisability of psychotherapy are pointed out in the discussion which follows each story. Certainly those patients who explicitly sought a new solution or perspective were offered psychotherapy. Such treatment is not recommended, however, for long-term drug- or alcohol-abusers who do not themselves request assistance. Nor is therapy advised for chronic patients who manage their disabilities. Problems are not suggested to patients who cope with their symptoms to their own satisfaction, by their own means. On the other hand, patients such as chronic arthritis sufferers may, at times of severe pain and disability, seek special or new forms of assistance for managing their discomfort. Also, previous drug- or alcohol-dependent persons can and do request psychotherapeutic assistance, as in the case of an ex-alcoholic who wanted help in preparing for reconciliation with his wife. Brief therapy at Laegernes Hus, in short, has been offered or recommended in those cases where it was considered to be a useful complement or adjunct to medical treatment.

Opposition to psychosocial programmes in primary health care states that attention to non-physical factors threatens disregard or mismanagement of somatic complaints. This is a realistic criticism and warning (Marenker 1976). The development of the counselling practices at Laegernes Hus lead to fuller recognition of the importance of listening and valuing the patient's descriptions of discomfort, its physical location and nature, the demands it makes of the patient's life, and other attending effects. The physical symptom is always taken seriously. To repeat, brief therapy was not sold as an alternative treatment, but rather offered as a complement to medical management of the patient's problem.

Laegernes Hus is a primary health care clinic (also referred to as a general medical practice) in western Denmark. In the early 1980s, the staff comprised four general practitioners, three health visitors, a midwife, and a physiotherapist, whose salaries were covered by the Danish National Health Service. Two nurses, a nurse's aide, one psychotherapist and an administrative staff of six were paid as employees of the clinic. Billund, the town where the clinic is located, has a population of 3000. In serving the outlying areas, Laegernes Hus carried around 4700 patients on its books.[1]

Medically, the clinic was supplemented by five general hospitals and two psychiatric hospitals within a radius of 35 miles of Billund. Specialist services — orthopaedic, cardiac, ontological, ear/nose/throat — were located in nearby larger towns. Educational, psychological and social care facilities were administered by local authority services in the area.

When the practice moved into its new purpose-built clinic in 1975, the doctors and psychotherapist elected to include concern about the psychosocial context of the patient within the frame of treatment services offered by Laegernes Hus. The staff set a common goal to make patients, Laegernes Hus staff and other related professionals conscious of available resources and possibilities for keeping the population healthy, for treating illnesses, and for engaging with illness-provoking factors in the community. This policy has been carried out while continuing to provide all the traditional primary health care services. The practice, however, extended its services to include the innovative patient services listed below, and the brief therapy counselling programme. Training courses and workshops were also organized and located in the clinic for allied professionals. Course topics included brief therapy, family therapy, applied group work, bereavement work and divorce workshops.

The Danish health insurance, in co-operation with the Doctors' Union, has composed a list of health practices specifying those health services to be covered by the Danish Health Insurance and at what

4

payment scale. This list therefore defines the 'traditional' medical treatment practices offered by all physicians in Denmark, and the only ones for which they receive payment. Activities outside this list are deemed 'untraditional' or experimental.

From April 1982 to April 1985, Laegernes Hus received additional payment from its governing health authority, Ribe County Council, to carry out the 'untraditional' practices it had been developing since 1975, and for which it previously received no payment. It was granted this support on condition that a research team from the Danish Hospital Institute follow, describe and evaluate the work at the clinic.

At the time of writing, which marked the end of their first year at Laegernes Hus, the multi-disciplinary research team documented the following 'untraditional' activities carried out by the health care professionals at Laegernes Hus:

Activity	Laegernes Hus personnel involved
Family preparation groups	Physiotherapist, doctors, health visitors. Midwife did not participate in these groups
Periodic well-baby examinations in groups	Doctors and health nurses
Counselling psychotherapy	Doctors and psychotherapist
Counselling psychotherapy combined with physical treatment for seriously ill (e.g. cancer patients)	Physiotherapist and psychotherapist
Weight groups	Nurses and nurses' aides
Women's groups	Psychotherapist and two of the administrative staff
Widow/widower groups	Psychotherapist and doctors
Group for diabetic children and their parents	2 doctors — taken in shift
Support to the chronic or incurably ill and their nearest family, in the home	Doctors

This book presents some of the treatment initiatives which took place at Laegernes Hus from its inception in the mid-1970s, to the time of writing in the early 1980s.

Laegernes Hus was founded on two beliefs about people. First, that human beings want to be responsible — that is, to contribute to, as well as to draw upon community resources, and to participate in the development of self, family and community. Second, that people contain all possibilities, including the possibilities to be healthy.[2]

The formulation is admittedly simple. For the staff at Laegernes Hus it represented an attitude to patients, and directed an optimistic belief that patient contact – be it chronic, sporadic, regulatory, somatic or psychiatric – holds the potential for those patients to enhance their self-esteem, improve their knowledge of bodily operations, their social skills, and/or discover or increase awareness of alternative ways to negotiate their environment and social relationships. It is an approach to health and community care which asserts an active recognition of the relationship between the individual and his environment. The health of the individuals within the community is seen to express and influence the quality of this relationship. With such assumptions, traditional medical diagnoses cannot be accepted as limits to the improvement of patients' circumstances.

Problems and symptoms which patients present for medical treatment were accepted and managed as physical phenomena. In cases where the symptom or problem could be seen to have a genesis in personal behaviour patterns, family problems, conditions at work or school, or through other conflicts in the community, the possible influence of a non-physical factor was introduced to the patient. He, she or the entire family were invited or recommended to meet with the psychotherapist to discuss the usefulness of brief therapy.

The first cases dealt with by the psychotherapist in this framework tended to be practical ones: socio-economic difficulties accompanying infirm or disabled family members. Then cases came through the school doctor in the form of recommendations to parents. These recommendations were based on physical symptoms, behavioural problems, or manifestations of anxiety or other distress in school-children. School doctors are not allowed to treat children at the school in Denmark, so the suggestion that parents and children visit their GP as a family created the natural introduction for contact.

The psychotherapy programme progressed to include referrals from Laegernes Hus doctors, from local authority sources (social services or day care facilities), and from patients in the area who heard of the possibilities for treatment or counselling. Friends, neighbours, health visitors and a local hairdresser (who never herself came for help) became referral sources.

Over a four-month observation period in 1979, when the programme had been in progress for three years, of 22 families seen in treatment, 19 were referred by the general practitioners and three by the school psychologist or headmaster. Of 54 individual clients seen in treatment in this period, 30 were initially referred by the GPs, 3 were self-referred, and 21 were individuals who returned for short term contact having had family or individual therapy at some earlier time (Laegehusgruppen 1980).

In the calendar year 1982, patient contacts were recorded by Laegernes Hus as raw data for the Danish Hospital Institute project. Of 4796 patients on the register, 253 patients participated in either the family preparation group or well-baby examination groups, and 155 patients took part in some other form of 'untraditional' treatment: weight groups, women's groups, widow/widower groups or brief therapy.

The variation of problems presented and the modes of actual referral or introduction are represented throughout the stories. Treatment contracts ranged from one meeting to a maximum of ten meetings. Laegernes Hus maintains an open-door policy of allowing patients to recontact — in line with the nature and practices of a primary health care clinic — but therapeutic encounters were defined as coming to a close after five to ten meetings.

Ellen Jespersen has from the outset of Laegernes Hus' programme defined and embodied the innovative role of psychotherapist in the primary health care setting. P.F. Pegg has been consultant to the integration of Laegernes Hus' psychosocial practice from its start, and has supervised the family therapy and brief therapy carried out in the clinic. Both work together and individually as trainers and consultants to medical, psychiatric, education and social service agencies.

Since our intention was to create a useful document about how a single-handed therapist can work with individuals and families, the material throughout the stories is presented through the 'I' of a single therapist. We aimed to contribute to the field by describing how existing principles of psychotherapeutic practice have been adapted to the demands of a general practice.

Within memory the social supports, social mobility, and expectations of assistance and care have altered drastically. The size and structure of schools have expanded. The role of the church and its personnel have dwindled. Commuting to work and special activities have cut down time with family and friends. It is arguable that one of the roles which has not altered so dramatically is that of the family doctor. People still visit their general practitioners not only in times of physical distress, but also when other openings for succour seem unclear or unavailable (Byrnes and Long 1976).

The methods developed and used at Laegernes Hus suggest a rethinking of the role, aims and purpose of psychotherapy in assisting people and, specifically, in relation to medical practice. This book does not advocate a psychotherapist for every general practice, but rather attempts to introduce new perspectives: to general practitioners, and indeed to all those who work in jobs where they are responsible for helping or influencing members of the general public.

This book is offered as a statement against the movement towards a specialized culture where each family has its own family therapist. It urges a notion of community in which those employed to assist others (and the number continues to grow) are attuned to possibilities within the community, its individuals and the social networks which comprise and serve both; and which values the ordinary patient, client or consumer by giving him the responsibility that is his.

Notes

1 Laegernes Hus in Billund was built in 1975 and is 625 square metres in area. The practice includes both town and country populations and is comprised of four physicians in partnership with regard to both patients and financial structure. There are 4700 patients belonging to the practice and these include residents of Billund and Egtved kommunes (municipalities or local authorities).

The Team
The work in Laegernes Hus is carried out by a multi-disciplinary group which consists of:

    3 public health nurses
    1 midwife
    1 physiotherapist
    1 family therapist
    2 nurses
    1 nurses' aide
    6 secretaries
    4 physicians

Employment and Salary Conditions of the Team The four physicians are paid by the public health insurance and all work full time.

The six secretaries are paid by the physicians (after an agreement with the commercial and clerical union) and are employed respectively 30, 30, 22, 20, 15 and 12 hours per week, plus relief (coverage for relief help when these are sick or on holiday).

The two nurses are paid by the physicians and employed for 37 and 9 hours per week respectively, plus relief.

The nurses' aide is paid by the physicians and employed for 24 hours per week.

The three public health nurses are employed by the kommunes (Billund and Egtved). Although their offices are located in Laegernes Hus, they primarily work in the field. Their active participation in Laegernes Hus consists mainly of the children's examination, pregnant groups, and full staff conferences.

The midwife is employed by Ribe Council (county council) and holds consultations for pregnant families in her office at Laegernes Hus once a week.

The physiotherapist functions as a private practitioner and is paid by the public health insurance. She holds consultations for patients in Laegernes Hus every day and works about 20 hours per week.

The brief/family therapist works approximately 18 hours per week in Laegernes Hus and is paid by public health insurance for her activities in connection with the three-year research project being carried out by the Danish Hospital Institute.

Physical Frames The physical frame in which the team is working is a 625 square metre single storey building, where the waiting-room takes up the central space. The waiting-room has been designed so that it can easily be emptied of its furniture and used for group activities such as family preparation groups, children's examinations and as a plenum room for meetings, courses, and so on. Lighting is installed in the ceiling so that the centre of the room may be used for video recording.

The rooms that are used by the midwife, the public health visitors and the family therapist are rented by the local authority and the council. The physiotherapist, as a private practitioner, rents the rooms that are used for physiotherapy.

Mobile video equipment has been installed in the family therapy room. There is a Xerox machine in another room.

[Translated from the Danish Hospital Institute research team's first end-of-year report.]

2   This description of the fundamental principles of Laegernes Hus, and their rationalization, is translated from *How Can the Role of Treater be Changed?* (*Hvordan Aendres Behandlerrollen*), written by the Laegernes Hus Group and published by The Doctors' Union, 1980. The 'we's' and 'our's' in this chapter refer to Laegernes Hus staff rather than to the authors:

"Fundamental Principles
The members of the group were engaged to different degrees in shaping a clear statement of the fundamental principles, but we have agreed upon the following:

> Human beings want to be responsible, and have within them all possibilities, including the possibilities to be healthy.

These fundamental principles are held with regard to our patients, to internal relations within the staff group and in relation to other professionals. The words 'want to' are significant to this formulation, as they convey the potentiality for positive action. In other words, we hold that if a human being appears irresponsible this is due to outside factors which prevent him from being responsible, or it is because he has not yet learned how to be responsible. The phrase 'have within them all possibilities' can be questioned in cases of the chronically disabled, dying patients, or persons with congenital handicaps. However, personal experiences have shown us that even persons limited by such circumstances are capable of personal growth. And so the group sets forth this statement as the affirmative expression of its ideals.

We want to work to a model of health rather than existing disease models. We have been unable to use the World Health Organization's definition in practice, and instead have agreed upon the following definition:

> Health means listening to one's body signals, and using them for development of oneself and the relation to other people.

It is important for us to place the concept of body at the centre of this definition. It is possible to relearn to use one's body consciously. By this we mean to open oneself to the experiences of the senses and to use one's knowledge and these experiences for personal development. The body provides symptoms — headaches, stomach aches, fatigue, neck pains, muscle tensions — as signals or direct warnings. If we learn to interpret these symptoms as indicating some imbalance or malfunction in the system — with regard to self, work, or in relations with others — then the understanding and realization can be translated into growth and change. In accord with this fundamental principle, we must regard our task first as teachers, then as treaters. Our common aim is:

> To work in order to make patients, ourselves and other professionals conscious of their own resources, and the possibilities to remain healthy. And at the same time, to treat illness, and to engage with the illness-provoking factors in the society."

2 The model

Brief therapy is the model of psychotherapy which was adopted for the psychosocial treatment programme at Laegernes Hus. Brief therapy was seen to be compatible with, and to express the fundamental principles at Laegernes Hus: of perceiving patients' symptoms as signals which admit opportunities for them to improve their means of meeting physical and psychological needs, for solving problems, and for participating in their social networks.

Family therapy contributed to the field of mental health by focusing attention on observable behaviour and its influence on family members and amongst them. Problematic or disturbed behaviour was seen as a social phenomenon, rather than as reflecting individual mental deterioration or deep-seated neurosis. Family therapy practices were based on the belief that positive change could be brought about by altering the family system. Some schools of family therapy maintain that family dysfunction is a fundamental aspect of the family system, and that improvement requires fundamental changes in the system. Another school, however, has concentrated on family interactions (the observable behaviour of which a family system is comprised) as the key to solving problems requiring treatment. They proposed that the most effective way to bring about a positive outcome was to alter interactions which could be seen to create or prolong the problem the patient presented. It did not appear to be necessary to make fundamental changes in the family system. In fact, once a problem was solved, subsequent changes could often be observed to occur throughout the system. This sort of 'knock on' effect can be seen in many of the stories.

The brief therapy model that evolved from this thinking made it possible to apply the method to individuals or family subsystems (Weakland *et al.* 1974).

This chapter will outline aspects of family therapy which informed practices at Laegernes Hus, and it will describe in detail the brief therapy model which provided the basis for the psychosocial treatment programme there.

Family Therapy in General Practice
That the patient is signalling some difficulty or dysfunction in the family, is a basic tenet of family therapy. General practitioners

encounter innumerable patients whose problems or symptoms can be directly attributed to family dilemmas. The stories amply demonstrate patients who turned to their doctor for help with problems directly or indirectly related to family circumstances. An example from the early days of the programme which illustrates this simply is that of a single mother who came for treatment for a bronchial complaint. Exploration of her circumstances revealed that her smoking had more than doubled in reaction to signs of youthful rebellion in her eldest daughter. Physicians are also the bearers of news which can precipitate family crises: pregnancy, malignant disease, symptoms which demand modification of diet or life-style. Familiarity with principles and practices of family therapy therefore seemed an apt accessory for the issues encountered in general practice.

Early in the integration of the treatment programme at Laegernes Hus, attempts at counselling on the part of the GPs resembled the traditional remedial model: instructions, advice, social prescriptions. Take it easy . . . try to eat a little less . . . what your child needs is more . . . . As the approach became better understood, it became clear that consultations benefited from acquaintance with the significance of family dynamics and social context. It was also evident that in a general, open-door setting, it would not be possible or practical to draw the entire family in each case. But useful interventions could be made with those family members willing and interested in change (Fisch *et al.* 1982; Haley 1976; Madanes 1981). Brief therapy had found its place in primary health care at Laegernes Hus.

Problems as Mishandled Difficulties
A key concept of brief therapy, which we believe makes it particularly applicable to general practice, is that problems are regarded as the consequences of mishandled difficulties:

> to become more specific, at this point we must add our clinical experience to our general views of behaviour and interaction. This experience has indicated over and over . . . that something in people's attempted 'solutions', the very ways they are trying to alter a problem, contributes most to the problem's maintenance or exacerbation . . . . Problems begin from some ordinary life difficulty, of which there is never any shortage. More often, though, the beginning is likely to be a common difficulty associated with one of the transitions regularly experienced in the course of life — marriage, the birth of a child, going to school, and so on. (Fisch *et al.* 1982, p. 13)

Viewing problems in this way provided a useful operational concept for work in a setting where diagnostic labels are traditionally — and as quickly as possible — applied to symptoms and problems. The story of Tom shows how easily a relatively common complaint — insomnia — can be rendered a medical or psychiatric disorder, and how brief therapy prevented his story from crystallizing at that point where his problem seemed the centre of his existence.

12

Tom claimed that he had not slept for the past 10 years. He had a job as a clerk, and for all practical purposes functioned responsibly from day to day. But he kept returning to his GP for help with his sleep. Tom was not a bad-looking fellow — a bit thin, with considerable dark circles under his eyes. He did tend to stare at people. He assured me that he had had psychiatric treatment some years earlier, and he therefore fully understood the cause of his sleeplessness. That was no problem.

When he was a child, there was a period when his father worked in another part of the country. He recalled that his mother was troubled by this, and at that time Tom began to wet the bed. He eventually stopped. But later, as an adolescent, and once again in a troubling situation, he feared reverting to this embarrassing habit, and so he stopped sleeping altogether. And, he claimed, he had not slept since . . . . Nor had he painted, he added as a dramatic afterthought. That had been an activity which had given him many happy moments in a rather lonely adolescence.

When I asked him how his life was — whether he had, for example, a girlfriend, he told me that he had one once, but only for a very brief time. 'How could I blame her for not being able to stand a boy friend who was tired all the time?'

Tom's goal was simple, though it did not seem that way to his GP. He had continued taking the variety of medication he obtained while in psychiatric care. But the sleeping pills did not help him to sleep. In his first and only session, we talked about his appearance and his weight. I mentioned cooking as a social skill. Since he could not sleep he might as well have late-night dinners with friends — to use those meals to develop friendships. I told him he could practise cooking at night. Why not get up when he couldn't sleep and prepare some exciting dish which he could take to work as lunch the next day. I also told him he ought to buy a painting kit, but not to use it. He was obviously not quite ready. One needed energy to paint, though not necessarily to cook, I said, as so many overworked housewives proved each day.

Tom did not return to our follow-up appointment. But one day a few weeks later, his doctor grabbed me in the hall. He demanded to know what I had done to Tom. Tom returned to visit his doctor; he looked much healthier. He claimed he still couldn't sleep, but he had become involved in a cooking club. And he spoke of joining an art class with one of the new mates whom he had met there.

The Purpose of Therapy
The purpose of therapy is to alter the behavioural, cognitive, or affective response of the patient to the difficulty, physical ailment, transitional crisis or other circumstances, which either creates or maintains the problem state. The therapist works to set clear goals, to

13

discover in what ways the patient is perpetuating the problem he defines or preventing himself from reaching his goals, and to help the patient to change his approach so that the problem is solved or the goals achieved.

The 'or' here is significant. For it can occur that when a goal is achieved, then the problem 'disappears' or ceases to exist as a problem. A young mother sought help with her 3-year-old son. He was waking her at 3 and 4 a.m. demanding breakfast. He had begun soiling himself. If he did not get what he wanted, he would scream and throw himself on the ground.

Hannah visited a child psychologist who referred them for family therapy. She was a young mother alone. Her husband was in prison and she had shifted home in order to be nearer to him. She worked to support herself and her son, and she travelled by bus each weekend to visit her husband. She was coping practically and economically, she said. But her little boy's behaviour puzzled and frightened her. She did not know what to do with him.

The little boy attended all four sessions. After obtaining a specific description of the boy's disturbing behaviour and her attempts to deal with him, therapy focused on Hannah's concerns. These were reframed as the goal of her wanting to be a better mother. She was instructed to take a set time each evening after work to talk and play with her son. She was coached and supported in setting realistic limits and in saying 'No' clearly to him.

It was stressed that to be a good mother she would also have to learn to take better care of herself. Hannah was directed to become better acquainted with the people in her house where she and her son had a room. In her third session plans were discussed concerning ways in which she could feasibly engage in relaxing activities with adults she knew. She was praised and encouraged for the examples she provided of both enjoyable and limit-setting behaviour with her son. In the fourth and final session, Hannah reported that he had slept through all nights but one in the past two weeks, had stopped soiling himself, and that she was surprised and satisfied in her increasing ability to communicate approval and disapproval to him.

The process by which difficulties become problems which require or are believed to require professional assistance is the focus of this therapy. Tom's story illustrates the importance of collecting sufficient information from the patient. The likelihood of Tom's sleep (as that of most patients who complain of total lack of sleep) was not the point. The therapist needed to discover how Tom defined his problem, and in what way his management of it prolonged the original difficulty as a chronic problem. It is this aspect of behaviour — the management of a difficulty — that brief therapy aims to alter.

It is always assumed that the behaviour which creates, maintains or exacerbates the problem is purposeful in the understanding of the patient, and represents the patient's best attempt to solve his difficulty. This assumption is exercised in all cases, even those with bizarre or seemingly incomprehensible behaviour, or where behaviour appears destructive to self or others. Problem-maintaining behaviour may be considered by the therapist as inappropriate or the wrong way to go about solving a problem, but not as pathological or expressive of some deep-seated need (Fisch *et al.* 1982; Haley 1976 and 1980; Madanes 1981; Minuchin, Rosman and Baker 1978; Minuchin and Fishman 1981; Watzlawick *et al.* 1974; Weakland *et al.* 1974).

It can happen that once a patient's goals are clarified, the situation is restructured so that a solution to the problem becomes clear. Superficially Jenny's circumstances resemble those of Hannah. Jenny's story demonstrates goal setting as a developmental process in psychotherapy. Contact was initiated because of physical symptoms. It resulted in the patient redefining her objectives, altering her behaviour and surrendering her client status.

Jenny was presented as a case at one of the Monday staff conferences. She had over the past year suffered a variety of complaints: migraine, stomach ailments, menstrual problems, back troubles. She had lost a lot of time at work due to sick leave, and there was now a danger that she might be fired from her job.

At the age of 22 Jenny came to Billund, expecting her first child. Her parents could not understand her wanting a child without a proper home or even a father with whom to raise it. But Jenny did not see it that way. She found herself a job as a cleaner. And despite a hard, unsatisfying job, and raising her son on her own in a tiny flat, Jenny had as active a social life as anyone could expect in a small rural community such as Billund.

Jenny had learned that with her background — eldest of eight children, father with periods of unemployment, Jenny herself receiving formal school supervision for bouts of truancy in her adolescence — and her current physical symptoms, she might qualify as disabled. As such she was eligible for a place on a rehabilitation course and a weekly allowance. She only required medical verification of her condition.

None of the staff wanted to see this 25-year-old legitimized as a chronic patient. When I met Jenny, I made clear that I could not contribute to keeping her a patient in the eyes of the state, and that I would not acknowledge her condition unless she could convince me she was really ill. Jenny consented to my terms. She believed in her illnesses, and was sure she could provide the evidence to validate her status as a disabled person.

At the end of the first session, Jenny was instructed to make a list each day of every single symptom she had. She returned next week with a long list. There were many different symptoms on the list, and each of them occurred almost every day. I told her the list was not

15

enough to convince me that she was disabled. In the week that followed she was to continue recording the symptoms, and also to record how she felt, or what was taking place when the symptoms occurred.

Jenny returned with a new list and an observation. One morning she suffered such a bad migraine that she was unable to take her little boy to day care. But as soon as she made the decision not to take him, she noticed, the symptom disappeared. We discussed symptoms as messages from the body — as signals of stress, or reminders, or as distractions from unpleasant events. The notion made sense to her. She talked about being scared to go back to work, and that she was also scared about getting fired.

'If you really want to become healthy enough to go back to work, what has to be different?' Jenny did not know the answer, but she volunteered two things that were stopping her. One was a guilty conscience over her dirty, disorganized home. She felt a bad mother in terms of domestic organization (her term). She was always too tired to start any job, or any kind of housework.

The other thing that made her guilty was what led to her missing the next appointment with me. The hospital had called her up from the waiting-list for an exploratory operation. The results of the examination were negative. The hospital told her she was healthy. But what ought to have been good news was not, for she got the message from the examining doctor that he considered her to be a hypochondriac. The day after she received this medical report was also the day she was due to return to her job. That day Jenny was fired.

During Jenny's next session, I asked her to list what she saw as the personal benefits of her illnesses, and left her to work on her own in my office for 20 minutes. The list was lengthy. As a healthy person, she might not have the same or as many privileges which her symptoms allowed, but I asked if she could imagine any. Before she had time to answer, she was instructed to bring to her next session a description of the mother she wanted for her little boy when he was 10 years' old.

And out of that task came Jenny's goals. The picture she painted of herself in seven years time was as an acclaimed fabric designer, living in a charming flat filled with her designs and many other lovely objects. She envisaged a circle of friends reciprocating her own generosity and affection. She saw herself healthy, attractive and still alone — with no particular mate for herself, no brother or sister for her son.

Becoming a fabric designer was a dream Jenny had harboured for years. She even knew where she wanted to get her training. From that point, my role shifted to that of advisor — helping her map out a study programme for the basic qualifications to the school of design, and assisting her application for financial support. And Jenny's role shifted from potential chronic patient to full-time student.

Jenny's story illustrates the power which clarification of goals has in therapy. Attempting to solve problems before they are intelligible or before goals are clear, is a common basis for the failure of the therapist to help her patient.

Organizational studies of success in goal attainment identify lack of clarity of purpose or goal as one of the major contributors to failure (Argyris 1970 and 1974; Hill 1977). It cannot be repeated too often that attempting to solve the patient's problems before comprehending the patient's view of the problem, specific details of the relevant issues, and the patient's notion of what constitutes progress is one of the most common reasons for the failure of the therapist to help the patient.

Identifying Patterns that Mean Problems
A necessary skill in brief therapy is to be able to identify what the patient is doing that causes problems or hinders them from being resolved. Inherent in this approach is the belief that individuals are as capable of solving predicaments as they are of making problems of them.

Since the model focuses on the patient's social interactions, the therapist's assessment of problem-creating factors must take into account the patient's social network. This extends beyond the family to neighbours, friends and acquaintances, colleagues, even to other professional helpers. The brief therapist acknowledges the social network as the context in which the patient expresses herself. It is the field in which she receives feedback on which notions of self-worth are based.

Social network provides the setting where regard of self and others is acted out, and tends to be the site where problems materialize, where solutions are discovered (Gottlieb 1981; Speck and Attneave 1973; Wallman et al. 1980). In Chapter 5, Susanne exacerbated the conditions which precipitated her exhaustion at work and social gatherings, as well as in her marriage. Alan and Henrietta's problems, seen in Chapters 4 and 5 were diagnosed in adult terms, but their own formulations stressed a lack of friends at school or at work as problematic. It follows that interventions aim to alter the patient's behaviour within their social contexts, and in the ways they relate to people around them.

This principle infers that a fundamental aspect of much problem-maintaining behaviour is its tendency to elicit inaccurate or negative feedback. Therefore, an underlying objective of therapy is to enable the patient to initiate or increase behaviour which raises self-esteem. This is held to be behaviour which fosters satisfying contacts in the social network and which the patient deems important. Furthermore, the principle reflects a moral stance of taking people at their worth, nurturing self-expression and self-esteem, and respecting differences in ways of seeing and living life (Frankl 1959; Glasser 1965; Haley 1973; Madanes 1981; Maslow 1976; Satir 1967; Weakland et al. 1974).

17

Learning to identify problem-maintaining behaviour means that the brief therapist becomes attuned to the ways in which people get themselves or keep themselves in trouble. The permutations of these social phenomena seem limitless. It is possible, we believe, and useful to refer to the broad categories of behavioural patterns which can aid therapists in spotting client's particular methods.

The way an individual perceives and defines a difficulty reflects his assumptions about it, and the way he will approach it. The patient's explanation of a problem and his rationale for handling it often reveals how the problem situation came about.

In 'Else's Husband' — Chapter 4 — Else's self-criticism prevented her from recognizing her accomplishments. Much of Else's past was spent helping others. Yet her retrospective analysis was that she had taken over or interfered in other people's lives. A considerable part of her present was absorbed in chewing over the past and trying to work out what she could have done differently. Her self-criticizing mechanisms filtered all feedback, and she was impelled to work even harder. This was the pattern which lead to her physical collapse, on more than one occasion. Else's pattern prevented her, as it does others, from seeing value or results other than failure. Problems accumulate, ever unresolved (Reusch 1973; Satir 1967 and 1972; Watzlawick *et al.* 1974; Watzlawick 1976 and 1977).

Defining issues in terms that are expansive, diffuse or multifarious is another way of keeping problems unsolved or goals unattained. This pattern reveals itself in discussion, as features of a problem seem to inflate, increase and shift. This phenomenon is frequently found in patients with generalized symptoms such as depression, anxiety, or non-specific body pains. The family in 'Closed Doors' in Chapter 8, demonstrates this pattern as they baffle the therapist with endless issues and often conflicting information.

It is important for a therapist to be able to recognize this pattern. 'Closed Doors' shows how easily a therapist can be diverted from assisting the client, effectively reinforcing the patient's belief that the situation is too complex to ever solve.

This pattern of dealing with problems is also demonstrated by professionals who classify patients as 'multi-problem'. The term denotes a client type with such onerous and insurmountable problems as to be resistant to all constructive assistance. Hence, this way of defining problems influences the expectations of the professional for the patient's improvement. As such, it affects the quality of service given to these patients.

Setting unattainable goals can generate problems. Trying to be the total twentieth century woman — wife, lover, housekeeper, professional, and more — had physical and emotional consequences for Susanne in Chapter 5. Parents seeking to be perfect parents — mature, youthful, authoritarian, matey, democratic — can also suffer problematic results (or their children can). Psychotherapists today contribute to this category of problem-maintaining behaviour. The therapeutic culture has nurtured a generation which expects that all problems can be resolved. Books, articles, workshops and television programmes create a contemporary expectation that total self-awareness and expression is possible, inherently desirable, and an ideal of human attainment. And many clients appear to believe that certain professionals hold the key (Lasch 1979). This is not to say that being idealistic or unrealistic always causes problems. Where this does cause problems, unrealistic goals — as in Lena's wanting 'real independence' in Chapter 5 — it is appropriate for the therapist to confront this pattern for the trouble which can result.

Problems are created through action. But of course, denying or refusing the presence of difficulties also constitutes problem-generating behaviour. Parents who believe they can divorce or re-marry without causing pain to each other or their children provide a contemporary illustration of this. Many patients deny the gravity or even the reality of their symptoms. Where symptoms do not receive adequate attention and care, the outcome can be grave (Friedman and Roseman 1974; Glass 1977; Lynch 1977; Metze 1981; Simonton *et al.* 1978; Schneider 1981).

Clinical experience in a general setting demands recognition that limited problem solving capacity can be the key factor in a presented problem. Because of limited experience, lack of knowledge, inaccurate feedback, or fear of trying something new (the list of reasons here is boundless), the patient may simply not possess the knowledge or skills to confront a difficulty, or to reach a goal in a successful manner (De Bono 1973; Grinder and Bandler 1975; Lakein 1974; Reusch 1973). When all persons seeking assistance are dealt with as requiring psychotherapeutic intervention, then the therapist underestimates this factor. In doing so she denies the potential of the client to learn and, further, threatens to professionalize needlessly and prolong the client's problem (Laurie 1974; Lasch 1979).

In the family work at Laegernes Hus, a frequent aim of the therapy was to realign confusion in the family hierarchy. Particularly where a problem involved a child, it was useful to see the situation in terms of family organization (Haley 1976 and 1980; Madanes 1981; Minuchin 1974; Minuchin, Rosman and Baker 1978; Minuchin and Fishman 1981). Experience with the families encountered in the practice suggested a recurring family pattern where parents were either over-involved or underinvolved with a child. This could occur in the sense of one parent embodying both under- and overinvolvement, or two parents complementing each other. The child in this situation receives a confusing mixture of very strict limits at some times and, at others, lax or unclear ones. Communication with, and responsibility for the child is confused. That child and his behaviour is often seen in these families to control what goes on in them. Or the child may take over a role of parent. Childlike behaviour, typical rebellion or naughtiness are often censured or interpreted as pathological or problematic.

Where this occurred parents were induced to improve the quality of their adult interaction and contact. They were encouraged to take responsible action as co-operating parents, and to relate to each other as peers and marriage partners. Tasks and homework were prescribed to instigate increased involvement between the underinvolved parent and the child about whom the family expressed concern. In addition, the child was prompted and encouraged in developing sibling and non-familial peer relationships (Haley 1976 and 1980; Madanes 1981; Minuchin 1974; Minuchin, Rosman and Baker 1978; Minuchin and Fishman 1981).

Where the therapist successfully influences the hierarchical organization of the family system, new responses and solutions are generated — other than those which have maintained the problem. Even where a child has been the introduction to family work, it is often the case that once the parental hierarchy is re-established, then the parents start to function more responsibly (Haley 1980; Minuchin, Rosman and Baker 1978; Minuchin and Fishman 1981). Once the generational boundaries are realigned, the therapist may work on setting future goals which assume the problem will no longer impede individual or family function, or development. The therapist may further underscore the differences between the generations by upholding the rights and obligations of childhood: not to be too perfect or grown-up, to occasionally be naughty, and to let adults have their own troubles.

Crisis Situations

Value has been found in distinguishing between everyday difficulties (such as Tom's insomnia or bed-wetting), the consequences of life transitions of an individual or family, intensified stress, and those difficulties which are brought about through crises, both physical and social, such as sudden death, divorce, abortion, terminal diagnoses, unemployment, bankruptcy.

The usefulness of this distinction is linked to special sets of physical or psychological shock reactions which accompany crisis. Considerable research has been carried out on the nature and extent of crisis reactions. The resultant literature provides guidelines for practitioners who work in settings where they are likely to encounter afflicted persons. These guidelines enable the therapist to identify reaction patterns and facilitate subtle and constructive intervention. Examples of this kind of work are elaborated in the stories (Cousins 1981; Cullberg 1975; Engel 1970; Keleman 1974; Krantzler 1975; Kubler-Ross 1969; Minuchin, Rosman and Baker 1978; Parkes 1972;

Pegg and Metze 1981; Schoenberg *et al.* 1970; Simonton *et al.* 1978; Weiss 1973 and 1975).

The Scheme at Laegernes Hus

Having discussed the aims of brief therapy, we shall outline the form which treatment followed at Laegernes Hus.

It seems worth noting that brief therapy principles were progressively adapted to suit primary health care and the patient population. The reader is encouraged to pursue the sources which appear in the Bibliography, for more fully developed theoretical background and other examples of application.

The discipline of counselling and psychotherapy is riddled with debate over the benefits and disadvantages of eclecticism. We have already indicated that the work carried out at Laegernes Hus, while fundamentally using the brief therapy model, respected and drew from various therapeutic models and techniques. Syntheses of models were devised to form the best possible response to patient circumstances. We argue this must always be the case. Attempts have been made to explain where other models or approaches are drawn upon in the case stories.

The general format for psychosocial intervention at Laegernes Hus was as follows:

Obtain Information to Formulate the Problem   This must include concrete, specific details of the symptom or difficulty for which the patient has sought help. What are the circumstances that lead to the patient seeking help from a doctor or psychotherapist just now? How does the symptom or difficulty 'fit' into the patient's life in relation to family, age, crisis, job, difficulties with responsibility, communication or social skills. What does the symptom or difficulty prevent the patient from doing or getting? The therapist aims to obtain sufficient information to establish an overall picture of the problem and explicitly seeks the patient's views to do this.

Formulation of the Problem   Therapist and patient work together to clarify the details of the problem, to determine in what ways it is a problem, and for whom it is a problem. When does the problem occur? When is it most noticeable or painful? It can be useful to evaluate benefits and disadvantages of the symptom or problematic circumstances.

Discovering the patient's notions of accountability can likewise be relevant. How did the problem arise? Is the problem a hindrance to some other activity, or the by-product of certain actions? Does the patient perceive it as caused by his or her own actions, or as the consequence of others — or as the will of God?

In What Ways has the Patient or Family Attempted to Deal with or Solve the Problem?   Here the therapist obtains specific details of

21

attempts to deal with or solve the symptom or problem: who is involved, what is done, how, in which manner, at what times, and to what effect? Obtaining specific details at this step is important for several reasons. In the patient's description of attempts to solve the problem, the therapist can usually discover what is being done which prolongs or exacerbates it. This information also provides clues to the limitations and potential of the patient's problem-solving capabilities, perception or knowledge of resources within the family or community, and the extent to which these resources are employed.

These details are necessary to enable the therapist to devise an intervention which alters the patient's behaviour or cognitive or affective responses, so that he or she is better able to manage the symptom or problem.

This is a key stage of brief therapy, and it is well to remember the 'rule' that methods which the patient or family have already unsuccessfully employed should not be tried or prescribed again.

Formulation of a Goal or Solution which is Acceptable to the Patient
Effective goal setting is a fundamental skill for most directive psychotherapies.

The therapist clarifies with the patient or family what would be construed as evidence of progress in therapy. What would constitute a desirable change or difference?

Where psychosomatic distress is evident, patients frequently express disappointment or anger about what they perceive as a gap between their needs or wants, and the circumstances they face each day. Some of the stories show how discussion about the patient's hopes and how he or she might begin to work to achieve them, can influence a positive outcome.

What would the patient consider the start of positive development?

The methods employed to formulate goals are basically the same as those used to formulate the problem. The therapist takes the necessary time, and demonstrates understanding, lucidity and intelligibility. It cannot be assumed that goals can be always set in a first meeting. Lack of clarity or cognizance can be the very reason an individual is in need of professional assistance. A primary objective of this work is that the individual's goals be clarified, restructured or refined into realistic and attainable terms.

This is not to say that the goals set for the patient are always set *by* the patient. The therapist may end up shaping the goals — for a number of reasons: overwhelming confusion or disorganization of the patient, conflict between family members, or inability of the patient to see beyond immediate problems or symptoms, to name a few. By challenging the ways in which the family members or individual patient perceive reality, the therapist can open possibilities for new ways of seeing and confronting a problem. In all cases, however, the information obtained about the patient's goals, hopes or potential solution to the problem advises the direction of therapy and the form of intervention.

Useful guide-lines in obtaining this information include requiring the patient to make positive statements of goals ('I want . . . ' rather than 'I don't want . . . ' or 'Never again . . . '). Goals or solutions should be formulated so that the means to reach them are within the ability or control of the patient. As far as possible, success should not be dependent on other persons, agencies, the weather (*not* 'I'll start exercising tomorrow. If it doesn't rain').

Goals should also be expressed to include some indicators for measurement of success — so that the patient can recognize to what extent, or whether the goal has been attained ('I did it!'). And of course, the priority is that the goal has meaning in the patient's world rather than that of the service agency or psychotherapist.

Intervention   Intervention is the means through which the therapist influences the patient to bring about behavioural, cognitive or affective change. Intervention does not necessarily aim to solve the problem presented by the patient, and should not automatically be formulated to do so. This is not to say that an intervention cannot assist the patient in solving the presented problem. But the purpose of intervention is to alter the response to the difficulty, physical ailment, transitional crisis, or other circumstances which make it worse.

Therapeutic interventions aim to alter the relationship between the problem state and the patient's goals by introducing new behavioural responses.

The word intervention denotes a number of different activities which have a variety of objectives in the therapeutic setting. Some professionals claim that once a client initiates a bid for assistance, all actions on the part of the professional are interventions. Everything the professional does influences and informs the subsequent attitudes and actions of the client (Schein 1969). The actions of the therapist may be subtle, almost imperceptible, such as positioning the chairs in a family session. The therapist relating details of a comparable case as a parable may not seem like an intervention to the clients, but it can have considerable impact (Haley 1973). Or the therapist may instruct or engage the patient or his family in formalized, structured activities. These can involve one or more persons. They can be reflective and quiet, or rigorous, verbal or written.

Some interventions highlight the behavioural patterns of the patient to help the therapist — and occasionally the patient — to see more clearly what is going on which hinders progress. Other directives structure experiences to challenge actively or alter the patient's self-perception and interaction with those around him.

Examples of all of these appear in the text.

Directives or tasks can be prescribed by the therapist to restructure the experiences of the patient and his family so that old perceptions are challenged or influenced, new responses formed and alternatives discovered. There is no set formula about how to give tasks or even what their purpose shall be. Interventions are devised with regard to the patient or client family: content and form are formulated to suit the problem presented by the patient, and the particular behavioural, cognitive or affective factors which contribute to the problem.

Creative interventions use the patient's strengths and abilities either to solve problems or to develop and support constructive patterns or both.

A 6-year-old boy was brought in as a problem. His parents related the difficulties the personnel had with him in kindergarten. At home he hit his little brother and made one hell of a racket. His mother said she was at the end of her tether. Alfred, the little boy's father, thought his son was 'not that bad', but that he must get confused sometimes. Alfred said he and his wife had different opinions about how to raise their children. But he admitted that he took the easy way out. He generally let his wife take care of most things at home.

At the end of the first session, Alfred was given responsibility for the boy each day when he arrived home from work. He was to bathe him, play with him or read to him, and see that he received his evening meal. If the boy went to his mother, she was to send him back to his father for help.

At the second session, Alfred reported how much he enjoyed his task. Alfred could not himself read, which meant that he went to the library to get tapes of children's books they could listen to together. In just a week he had experiences with his son he had never had before. The couple also observed that when Alfred had responsibility in the home, his wife had to deal with him directly, This is precisely what they had been avoiding for a long time. And in this session they asked for help in improving their communication as a couple.

The task had interrupted the couple's current approach to their problem and supplied another. In fulfilling the task Alfred and his wife gained new information about the nature of the problem for which they originally sought help. They saw what it was that hindered them in dealing effectively with their son. Consequently, and in terms that held meaning for them, they redefined the problem and their goals.

No inherent merit is accorded to complex or unusual interventions. Since the purpose is to challenge accepted views and practices, sometimes the means to that may seem unprecedented or outlandish. It may seem to the novitiate that brief therapy is about devising the single, all-encompassing strategic intervention or task which leads to resolution and a successful completion of therapy. But the case studies should show that tasks or interventions are employed at all stages. Therapeutic intents include:

- Challenging the terms of the presented problem.
- Developing and encouraging more complex responses — which generally include augmenting the patient's intellectual and emotional responses.
- Challenging and stimulating alternative individual behavioural or interactional responses and, where appropriate, increasing participation in and use of the social network, as with Petra's relation to the community.
- Creating confusion or crisis so that a stalemate situation might culminate in a satisfying new conclusion.
- Permitting or formalizing pursuit of actions which the patient unsuccessfully resists.

Well-formulated interventions enhance the authority of the therapist and the client's belief that the therapist can help, and increase the likelihood that the client will try approaches directed by the therapist. 'Homework'-style tasks engage the patient beyond session time. Active interventions enable the patient or his family to feel they are contributing to the problem-solving process — even if they may not comprehend the purpose of the task from the start. It is important that tasks are activities that the therapist judges the patient can successfully carry out.

A primary rule of thumb in brief therapy relates to the use of tasks and interventions. Where an action is seen to be ineffective, it should not be tried again (Madanes 1981). Or as stated by Fisch *et al.*:

In our view, if at first you don't succeed, you might perhaps try a second time — but if you don't succeed then, try something different (1982, p. 18).

Before going into the case studies, we shall clarify a few points about the style and presentation. To protect the interests of the patients and clients, all the stories are masked. Anyone who has lived in a small community will know that the incidents which occur make participants in local history readily identifiable. Of course, we have been selective in retaining and presenting the salient points of each tale.

This very selectivity is a primary element of psychotherapy, for in exercising selective attention to, and use of detail in, an individual's life — isolating some features and expanding others — the therapist progresses in his craft to help his patient discover the answer to 'what comes next?' And it is in regarding psychotherapy as seeking a creative answer to this question, which lies at the heart of a practice where patients' lives are respected for the whole that they constitute, rather than as suitable cases for treatment (Forster 1974).

3 Life transitions

Robert and Anne

'Here is Ellen's room,' said the doctor as he entered my room with a tall attractive man in his early fifties. 'Ellen, this is Robert. I have told him that I think he might be able to learn something from you.' And with that, he slipped out and closed the door behind him.

'I'm not sure why he brought me here,' Robert said without moving towards the chair I offered him. 'I came to see the doctor because of pains in my chest.' He indicated his area of pain with a movement of his hand.

'I realize he had examined you . . .'

'Yes, and he said that nothing serious was wrong.' Robert paused. 'But he did mention something about stress . . .' His voice trailed off, but he still did not move towards the chair.

'Perhaps that's the reason he suggested you talk with me.' I took my own seat. 'In what ways could you be stressed?'

Robert sat on the edge of the chair. He looked at the door, and at the floor, then at me, and answered, 'I really don't see any reason to be stressed.'

I looked him up and down. 'How old are you, Robert?'

'I don't see any point in this . . . I am 52.' It was clear that he was still irritated. He could not see why the doctor had brought him here just now.

'What is your work?' He answered that he was a dentist. 'Have you got a particular speciality?'

He told me that he was interested in preventative work, and that he had made a number of innovations in that area of dentistry. As he described his work, I recalled that I had heard something of his work before, especially his work with children. He was liked by his patients and admired by many of his peers.

'Well, then I think I see the reason why the doctor brought you in here.'

For the first time he looked directly at me. He waited for me to elaborate my cryptic statement.

'We have been talking so much here at Laegernes Hus about how we could learn from dentists' work — especially your kind of work with preventative care.' Robert looked flattered at my comment about his work, and blushed a bit. I would learn that Robert blushed as quickly when he was angry as when he was pleased.

'But I still don't see what that has to do with my chest pains.'

'My guess is your doctor wants you to learn how to prevent a heart attack. Is that something you want to learn?'

'Yes, of course I want to prevent that, but I still don't see how I can learn that from you.' He was more impatient now than irritated. The polite edge in his voice hinted at condescension. He did not mean to hide it.

'Fine. It's fine that you want to learn that. But if I am to succeed in teaching you, I must see you together with your family. How many children have you?'

'I've got three, but they don't live at home any longer.'

'And what are their ages?'

'My son is 22. He's married now. And my daughters are 18 and 19.' He told me that they had just left home the previous summer, so I asked if he would return with his wife. 'But she hasn't anything to do with this. Our marriage is perfectly happy, and I love my wife very, very much.'

'Then I'm sure she won't refuse to come with you. She must be as worried as you about this chest pain.'

Before I saw Robert and his wife Anne a week later, the doctor told me that Robert had high blood pressure and had recently been frightened by a series of chest pains. I began our first session together by telling them that I often worked with couples in their circumstances. It wasn't so unusual for parents to come to the clinic for some sort of help around the time the last child left home.

I asked them if they would discuss together the last year the children had been at home, and then arranged their chairs so that they faced one another. Robert folded his arms and leaned back in his chair. Anne sat upright, her hands on her knees. She looked a bit scared.

'Well,' began Robert, looking at me out of the corner of his eye, 'of course we have talked about this many times at home, but . . .' And they proceeded. Through their brief conversation I learned how Anne had found a job as secretary at a local factory six months before the girls left home. Both of the girls had supported her very much. They helped with the housework, and also helped Anne brush up on some of the skills she needed in her job.

'I certainly couldn't have done it without them,' she said to Robert. 'You didn't help then, and you don't help now.'

Robert's disappointment in his son came across very clearly. The couple had evidently spoken of it often. I was to learn that in his first year of university studies, the son had met a girl. When she became pregnant, they married. The worst of the story seemed to Robert to be that the girl was older than Robert Junior, and was also the main financial support of the new family. Robert blamed Anne for encouraging what he saw to be shiftless behaviour in his son.

He further complained that both wife and daughters had never been accessible when he needed them. Anne was too busy with her new job, and her courses, and the girls were always out with friends. Underlying Robert's comments was a sense that he no longer found satisfaction in his work. Since starting her own job, Anne was not so interested in hearing about Robert's any longer. Her new occupation, and the course she had enrolled in to improve her position, took the time she once devoted to him.

After about 15 minutes of this uninterrupted discussion, the couple paused and looked at me. 'In couples where stress is a factor, it often can be that each individual isn't getting all they'd like from their spouse. It frequently happens in the sexual part of the relationship. How is that part going with you two?'

Both looked embarrassed and admitted that they had been scared by ·Robert's chest pains, so they had cut down that part of their relationship. Anne said his recent handicap was a physical reality she felt she had to tolerate.

The session ended in my giving them three tasks. The following week was part of the Easter break. I asked them to come with their two daughters, since both would be home on leave from school. Second, each of them should individually compose a list of three goals for the future. And finally, at least one time before the next session, they should have an argument of at least 20 minutes' length before they made love. Either of them could keep track of the time. The idea of homework startled them a bit, but they agreed to try their best.

The next session Robert and Anne arrived with Katherine and Christine. Katherine, 19, had begun studying psychiatry that autumn in Copenhagen. Christine, 18, had left home at the same time as her sister to attend a high school in another part of the country. The residential school specialized in drama and dance. Both girls gave a strong first impression of health and straightforwardness as they entered my office.

Both expressed their willingness to join their parents.

I began the session by asking the couple how the tasks went. We all laughed when they pulled out and presented their lists simultaneously. Robert insisted Anne read hers first: to join the local amateur drama club, to learn French, to start folk-dancing. Robert smiled patiently while she read. He paused, then read his: taking more time with Anne in the evenings, enjoying going to dental congresses with Anne, beginning to paint.

'You always talk about wanting to paint, Father,' said Christine. And Robert told how, as a young man he had wanted to go to art school and become a painter. But his father had thwarted this dream. He insisted that Robert acquire a profession.

'And I have several times been grateful to him for that. I wonder where you three would be today if I hadn't been able to give you such a good start in life.' Robert shook his head, finally, saying, 'You have to deny yourself something and resign yourself to things if you are to take good care of your family.'

I complimented them on fulfilling the first two tasks, and asked how it went with the third. 'We couldn't possibly do it,' replied Anne.

'Perhaps you could tell me more about that task,' I said, looking at Robert. They both took great pains to assure me that with Robert's condition, any overexcitement was unthinkable. 'So, there are things you want for yourselves which are difficult to obtain. You think, because there's not enough time, or you're afraid of some negative consequence, or perhaps because you're not sure what it is you want. You spoke last week, Robert, of wanting to have better contact with your daughters . . . .'

I instructed them to speak to each other in pairs, parent to daughter, in two corners of my office. They were to discuss what they had missed of each other, now they lived apart or spent more time apart, and what they might like to have together in the future, given the realities of their new lives. They did this for 20 minutes.

When they returned, each was asked to tell one thing he or she found most important with regard to what they felt they were missing, and one goal they hoped to attain with another family member. After everyone else had spoken, Katherine said that what she wanted to do with her father was to visit her brother in Copenhagen, so that he might at last see his grandson. Robert flushed red with anger when he repeated the tale of his son's marriage and lack of ambition. 'I can't bear to see him now,' he finished his story, looking at Katherine.

'Well, I understand that it's hard for you to see your son living in a way you cannot condone. Since it's also impossible to argue, and difficult to make love, then it might be much too painful for you to paint.

'But you have all of you spoken here today about things that you want to do with each other. Next week I want you to return and tell me how this vacation week has gone.

'And you, Robert, I want you in the next week to buy yourself painting gear. Everything you need to paint. I don't want you to even think of using it yet, but I do want you to buy it in the next week.'[1]

Robert was early for the next session. When I saw him alone, I was a little worried. His face was brightly flushed. I could not tell if he was angry or pleased about something. When I asked him where the rest of the family was, he told me they were coming by car. And he asked if I wanted to see his new bicycle. He described how Christine's boyfriend had come for dinner. Over the meal, the youth, who was a cycle enthusiast, talked Robert into getting a bike — for cheap transport, respect for ecology, and for improved health. 'He's a fine lad,' Robert said. 'And it's a marvellous bike!'

The whole family agreed they had enjoyed their week. Christine particularly was pleased that her father had for once seemed to enjoy the company of one of her boy-friends. In the vacation, we assessed, all four had seen new possibilities for a life where they could enjoy themselves as individuals. 'It's the nicest Easter I have ever spent,' Robert concluded.

I told Robert and Anne that I didn't want to see them until a month had passed. I wanted them to spend a weekend together somewhere away from home. I told them I knew they had the means, and that I knew they could take the time if it was important. I suggested that Robert decide where they should go, and make all the appropriate arrangements. I predicted that, over the weekend, they would probably have at least two serious quarrels, but that they should not worry over these. Such a reaction in these circumstances was not unusual. I finished the session by saying quietly but clearly to Anne, 'I think I ought to mention that the doctors here have been discussing and wondering about how sexual activity increases when people begin jogging or cycling.'

'It was good that you warned us about the quarrelling,' Robert began our next session five weeks later. 'We had a terrible fight in the hotel restaurant over Saturday lunch. Anne just walked out in the middle of it. At first I was so shocked I didn't know what to do.'

'But then he followed me back. He caught up with me before I reached the room.' They quarrelled in the hotel corridor, then shouted at one another in their room. 'Then at one point just before dinner time we looked at one another and burst into laughter.'

'And we spent such wonderful hours in bed.' Robert was shy and proud at the same moment. 'As we haven't since we were kids.'

I told them I was pleased to hear about their weekend. The purpose of this last session was to evaluate their work, and to give them the opportunity to discuss further hopes for the time to follow. Of particular interest was the symptom with which Robert was referred to my office the first time we met.

'The pains still come, but much less frequently. I have come to understand that when they occur, I have to find out what's stressing or worrying me. I've spent time thinking about it, and I can see that it either has to do with something that has happened, or things I expect to have to take care of. Seeing the difference between the two helps — at least as a starting-point.' Robert paused. 'I did buy the paints, as you said, but I haven't painted anything yet.'

I assured him that he was doing fine. Only he would know when it was time to begin painting. He should not begin before he was absolutely sure it was time. I gave them 15 minutes alone, and told them to work individually on making lists of the issues they would want to include if they were to draw up a contract between them: of items or issues they wanted individually, and things they wanted together from now on. Their contract should include everyday examples, as well as the broader points of living together.

When I returned to the room, we discussed what was on the lists. They were able to agree on the broader principles. It was the small details they were stuck on. Anne had spent many years in the waiting role — not sure what time Robert would be home from work, waiting to hear the results of his new projects. Now Robert was in that role, and he was insisting that she telephone him whenever she would be late. 'So there still are things you two have to work out together — openly — or there will be more difficulties.'

On Anne's list was a desire to visit Robert junior with her husband. Robert looked pained, and at first he did not respond. 'It's something I have to think about,' he admitted. 'But Anne, I'm not ready to see him just yet. I may be, but I need more time to think about it.'

I did not see them after that, but each week on Mondays and Wednesdays the clinic staff are involved in a lunch-time conference where they discuss problems, difficult or rewarding cases, share feelings about experiences with patients, and feed in information about patients known to all. One of the doctors mentioned at conference some weeks later that he had taken Robert off his high blood pressure medication.

It is commonplace in medical anthropology that illness generally begins with the patient's attention to and perception of the early manifestations of disease, and his subsequent presentation of self. 'Personal and family beliefs and experiences, and through them culture and social systems, are powerful influences on these processes' (Kleinman 1980, p. 75; see also, Mechanic 1972; Parsons 1967). 'Psychophysiological disorders' in particular express the complex relationship between social or cultural variables, and physiological ones. These are disorders where a constant feedback between the somatic manifestations of disease and the patient's attention to and interpretation of these, influence the perception of self as healthy or ill (Kleinman 1980).[2]

In Susan Sontag's historical perspective of metaphors and attitudes related to illness, she writes that some diseases (and she writes particularly about tuberculosis and cancer) were believed to be handed down through the family and/or revealed something about the character of the sick person (1979). Similar disparaging beliefs persist to the present day, where clinical decisions are based on family social or economic background, or where a symptom, such as alcoholism, attaches a stigma to its carrier.

At time of illness, individuals feel hindered or caught out by their bodies. They often feel exposed, failures in the fight to meet life's challenges. Patients or their families frequently express a feeling of blame for being, or pretending to be, ill.

These considerations about illness and patients inform the psycho-social counsellor in two ways. First, symptoms and illness need to be

31

reframed out of a pejorative context. They must be rendered in such a way that the patient can start to 'read' or 'use' their symptoms to advance or progress. It is vital when working within a psychosocial context not to accuse or imply pejorative overtones to the patient or the family. The therapist must approach this work with the assumption that at some level the patient's symptoms have meaning for him. There must be acknowledgement, either explicitly or implicitly, that most people are frightened by symptoms and want to be rid of them. This does not mean that it is absolutely necessary in successful brief therapy to discover a meaning or function for the symptom. The assumption underlies the work. The emphasis is on 'seeding' concepts that symptoms are more than physical faults to be repaired. The therapist must find a way to do this which makes sense to the patient.

The second consideration is to alter the communication or patterns of social interaction in which the symptom or illness serves a purpose. The process can be subtle or straightforward. The skill of brief therapy involves reframing behavioural goals for treatment so that the manifestations of illness and the sick role no longer hold prominence for the patient or the patient's family. The information obtained by asking the patient about his goals for treatment, his interests, his concerns, all contribute to the direction the therapist will follow. These details can be as important as those of the symptoms, as in Robert's case. In Jenny's case, discovering this information was an integral part of the therapeutic process. Engaging the patient in this process redirects the attention and efforts of the patient — and family — to transactions and pursuits which involve them in activities which do not emphasize or perpetuate the sick role.

It is common for the psychosocial counsellor to encounter reluctance, as demonstrated by Robert. Resistance, in the analytical sense, is not a useful concept in brief therapy. Reluctance is regarded as a normal reaction in most circumstances where psychotherapy or psychosocial counselling is suggested to persons who did not present themselves to request this form of assistance. It is believed there is little to be gained by patient or therapist by confronting the reluctance in these instances.

Robert and Anne's situation represents a case of life and family transition. Robert's age, the daughters leaving home, his physical symptoms are all signposts. At times of transition, the individual often presents himself as if in limbo. The individual who approaches his 'crossroads' problematically tends to evaluate — generally unfavourably — achievements and patterns of the past, and is unable to read any promise in the future. People in transition have an aura of loneliness about them: the lack of challenge in a job once exciting; sudden realization of offspring gone; friends who do not 'fit' any longer, who do not share or understand. All these can be experienced as serious losses. Given this confusion about the future and dissatisfaction with the past, it is not so surprising that people manifest physical symptoms at these points.

Transitions are times when people can make decisions about and plan for what they would want next in their lives. Sociologists and psychologists alike write about the disorganization and discomfort of these periods as powerful stimuli to change (Carter and McGoldrick 1980; Eisdorfer and Lawton 1973; Keleman 1974; Levinson *et al.* 1978; Marris 1978; Pressey and Kuhlen 1957; Sheehy 1974 and 1982).

If Robert had 'listened to his heart' he would not have had a romantic decade, but approached his sixties on tiptoe, the way many heart patients do (Lynch 1977; Metze 1981).

There are a number of ways to think about the events which preceded Robert's hypertension. Developments in brief therapy and problem-solving therapy have altered the therapist's approach to a patient with Robert's history. The brief therapist does not encourage exploration or expression of feelings which follow events such as his son's marriage, his wife's new career, his daughers' departure. Having the couple discuss these together allows the therapist to note factors which the couple deem relevant to their current situation, and to see how they interact in discussing these issues.

Inviting the whole family enables the therapist to have a picture of the family context, where tensions lie, what resources or limitations exist. Conjoint sessions make it possible to restructure the organization of the family. In this case, cross-generational discussion enabled parents and daughters to participate in an activity which acknowledged the daughters' more adult roles in the family.

By asking this couple to draw up a contract between them, I was asking them to consider consciously what they wanted for themselves as individuals, and for Robert and Anne the couple. Leaping to their sexual activity might seem the wrong way round, but discussing the sexual aspect of their relationship was strategic in refocusing their attention to an area most people want to improve. It also redirects concern away from Robert's chest symptoms. Openly discussing this topic served to communicate promise about their future.

Generally, it is not a good idea to prescribe complex or over-ambitious tasks. This couple was capable of separating and fulfilling the demands made of them. I knew it was important not to keep them in treatment longer than necessary. If anything, I wanted a 'too brief' contact, so they would know they could return without being landed with long-term therapy.

Lise's Child
Lise had been hospitalized for heavy bleeding and severe menstrual pains twice over the past 18 months. When she made another appointment for the same complaint, her GP advised her to ring for an appointment with me. Slim and neatly, if inexpensively dressed, Lise

33

was colourless in a way which made it difficult to see if she was unhappy or anaemic. She told me that she was 32. She told me she worked as a clerk-typist in the local tax office. And when I asked 'How can I help you?', she told me that she had supposed I knew everything from her doctor.

'But I don't,' I responded. 'Perhaps you can tell me about yourself.' She looked puzzled for a moment, as if not sure where to begin, then she told me about her four brothers. Lise was the eldest of a family of five. She was obviously proud of each of her brothers. Two of them were married — to well-educated women. They were doing well, but neither yet had any children. The two younger brothers were unmarried, she told me. One was at university, the other at technical college.

'And you?' I asked her. 'How about you?'

Lise had married at 20. For three years she had supported her husband in his medical studies. A year after he completed, Lise discovered, in a way which was even now too painful for her to describe, that he was having an affair with another woman, a nursing student at the hospital where he was located. Of course she divorced him. Then followed a period of brief affairs with many other men. She lived with one other for a short period before the man she was now with.

Michael, she told me, was part owner of a car repair business. They had been together for three years. They invested in a little house together. His business had grown slowly if surely. She herself had a job in the tax office. When I asked about her work, she said that it was the longest time she had held one job. With a little smile she added that she had recently received a promotion in her office.

'So the last three years have been good ones for you. How is it that I can help you now?'

'I don't know,' she started hesitantly. 'But . . . ' then she told me that she and Michael had long hoped to have a child. There had been many problems. She was now 32 and he 38. Both felt pressed to start a family as quickly as possible. After a year's trying without success, they had undergone fertility examinations. Nothing seemed to be the matter with either of them. The last specialist they had seen had put them on a scheme which included a daily recording of her temperature curve to determine her most likely time to conceive. They had followed the doctor's instructions faithfully, even through the heavy bleeding and pains for which she had been hospitalized. They had kept the curve for almost two years now.

'You must be disappointed having no result after such hard work.' When I said that, big tears formed in her eyes. 'I can see how very much you want a baby.' She continued weeping openly, if quietly. 'I'd like to meet you again. With Michael next time, because this concerns both of you.'

Compared to Lise's paleness, Michael was startlingly colourful:

blonde hair, bright blue eyes. He was short and slight and muscular. He looked directly at me and answered in an easy way.

Michael enjoyed his work very much. He spoke enthusiastically of the motor rallies he took part in on weekends, and preparations for them which he did with his friends in the workshop he owned. He hoped for a son with whom he could share his interest and his enthusiasm for cars. As Michael spoke, I could see in her smile and the way in which she followed the movements of his hands, that Lise also wanted a child for what she knew Michael would gain from being a father.

I commented again that it was clear they both wanted a child. I told them I knew how humiliating the fertility examinations could be, and that I appreciated how hard they must have worked over the past two years. I asked them to discuss together what they thought had hindered conception. I had the couple face each other and begin talking together.

'I am a single child, and so are my father and mother. I know they wanted another child, so I can't help wondering if I didn't inherit some hormonal imbalance. Even if they said nothing was wrong.' Michael paused, pondering and looking toward Lise. She seemed to look back at him, but her eyes were far away. Slowly the tears began to come, then faster and faster. Michael, shocked, looked at me, then back at Lise. He took her hand. He stroked it fondly. 'Don't cry, darling. You know that we can get married and adopt a child. I'm sure of that.'

Now Lise sobbed loudly. 'But I know it's my fault . . . .' She paused and he looked at me, appealing.

'Nonsense, darling. We know there is nothing wrong with you.'

'I've never told anybody.'

Lise was still crying, but a little more calmly. And then came her story. Before she knew Michael she had become pregnant by another man. Even if they both wanted the child he did not want to stay with her after her pregnancy. In spite of her great desire to have the baby, she decided to have an abortion. She couldn't see how she could take care of a baby alone. She cried very much at the time — before, during and after the hospitalization for the abortion. She felt strongly it was not the right thing to do. 'He was a real person,' she said. 'But I couldn't see any other answer.' She hid her face in her hands, and didn't appear to hear Michael's: 'But why didn't you ever tell me about it darling?'

Softly she added, 'Now each time I see a little boy of three, I think he might have been mine. I'm sure the baby was a boy.'

Michael put his arm around her and stroked her cheek with his hand. Neither of them said anything for a long time. She put her head on his shoulder. 'At the start they told me there was risk that I might become sterile. But afterwards, when I cried so much, they said that I would always be able to become pregnant again. I'm sure that I am the reason we can't get a child.'

Michael looked toward me again: 'Well, it's impossible to tell which theory is right. But I can't forget that you've been carrying all this alone for such a long time.' We all three of us sat silently for some moments. Then I told them what they had spoken of was very important. I told them to go home, and to throw away all the charts and the curves and the schemes, and just to take good care of one another. I told them to contact me in a month. Then I let them go home.

One day some weeks later, someone knocked on my door. I opened it to discover a beaming Lise before me. A little over a month had passed since I saw them. I didn't have time to ask her into my office before she declared, 'The urine test was positive!'

I have seen a big difference between women who have dealt openly with their abortions and those who try to hide them. I never try to convince a woman to share it with her husband, but the young woman who stood before me that day showed the mark of those who choose to be open. She was radiant with pleasure and with an assurance that the child within her was fresh and alive and would be born healthy in nine months' time.

Lise told me that if the test were positive, she and Michael had planned to go away for a romantic weekend to celebrate. So she was coming to say that they did not want to fulfil their appointment for a return session.

This story sounds simply too good to be true. It is true though.

It would have been possible to treat Lise's story as one of loss, or as grief work, standard post-abortion counselling. As she told her life story, though, with her emphasis on the educational, vocational and marital success of her brothers, it seemed to me that she evaluated her own history, and was dissatisfied with what she saw.

The stability she described in her current work, home and relationship suggested that she was at the crossroads of a discouraging past and a promising future. A baby would be the milestone of her success as a woman and as a mother. At times of transition, many people express ambivalence. This ambivalence can take many different forms. The story demonstrates the value of a simple intervention, that of assisting the patient to clarify her goals.

Lise's comments strongly implied that she knew what the problem was, even if she did not conceptualize the role her symptoms played in it. Her weeping in the first session revealed that she was carrying something very painful to her.

From my experience, most women in her situation react with irritation or with angry demands to be 'fixed'. An initial task of the therapist is to affirm the belief of both partners in their abilities to come through this difficulty.

The benefits can be seen here of meeting the partners together. I never encourage people to express or admit to feelings in sessions. Lise's story shows clearly that, given the opportunity, sorrow or guilt express themselves. Michael and Lise were particularly good at accepting each other's personal declarations, and supporting each other.

Some couples discover in the therapeutic setting that neither of them want a child at all. Both are willing to concede to parenthood because they believe it is important to their spouse.

The case provides the opportunity to explain about initial meetings with new patients. Some people in the community knew about my work. Others knew nothing about what I dealt with, or what 'psycho-social' means. On a first meeting, I presented myself as one with training and experience who could, and was willing to, help. I never tried to solve a problem before I knew what the problem was, or in what way a patient wanted help with it. And I did not formulate circumstances as problems which did not exist for the patient.

Patients often assumed I knew all their details from their doctor. I did not. Introductory referral comments and the sharing of information at staff meetings were meant to develop a full picture of the patient's circumstances, rather than to predetermine a diagnosis. Patients were regarded as the authority on their situations, and always encouraged to describe these as fully as possible. I did not read notes sent in advance from other agencies. The discerning professional is probably more often misled than assisted by this kind of information.

It is probable that most people see themselves through life transitions without ostensible professional assistance. Outside agencies generally become involved when a child presents a problem at a critical juncture in the family's developmental cycle. 'The Butcher's Wife' shows a case where the mother 'became' the problem when her last child was preparing to leave home.

The Butcher's Wife

One day a 16-year-old boy from a school in a nearby town came to me. He asked if I thought I could help him. He was leaving home next summer to go to a residential training college, and he was worried about how his parents would get on together after he left. Christian told me that he was the youngest of nine children, and for the past four years had been the only one living with his parents.

Over the past two years, Christian had seen his mother drink in a way he had never seen before. It scared him, and he had spoken with his older sister about it. She agreed that their mother needed help. He had seen his father shouting at his mother about the drinking, and he knew that this would not solve the problem. Christian knew of me from one of his schoolmates whom I had helped. He decided to come and see if I could do anything for his mother.

'I know how it is to be the youngest child, and perhaps the most important one in the family,' I said to him. 'I know too what it's like to be a mother sending her youngest from home. So if you can persuade your parents to come here with you, I might be able to talk with them. Telephone me after you have spoken to them.'

At the doctors' conference the following week, one of the doctors said that the butcher had been in to talk about his wife. Both the butcher and his wife were around 60. The butcher had told him that his wife had drunk on and off over the past two years, but recently the drinking had increased enough to worry him. The doctor told the conference that he had instructed the butcher to go home and talk with his wife about the two of them returning. He promised the butcher he would speak to me about seeing the two of them in treatment.

Christian had dark brown eyes beneath his glasses. His hair was short, brown with a tinge of red. He was as earnest in appearance as in the concern he expressed for his parents. Albert, the butcher, resembled no one so much as Friar Tuck. He was the proverbial neighbourhood butcher: short, round, with a little fringe of hair at the edge of his crown. His hands were sensitive and his dark eyes alert as he looked from his wife to his son to me.

His wife Betty was taller. She had big bones and looked more tired than thin. To me she looked scared at being there.

I began by asking Betty how they succeeded in bringing her. She said that she had never been able to deny anything either her husband or her children asked of her. She had always done everything she could for her husband and her children. I told her how brave I thought she was since she knew they might be talking about her as the problem.

I asked about her age. She said that she was 59, and had been married for 32 years. In that time, she and Albert had had nine children, each of them born whole and healthy and each now doing well. And she added proudly that Christian would be leaving home next summer to further his training. We agreed that it was a good result of 32 years of marriage. I asked Albert what he wanted out of treatment. He said that he wanted the problem solved. I asked him what problem he had. He replied that I and 'all the others' knew perfectly well that Betty drank too much. It was very difficult for him when he came in from the shop, which was only next door, and found her drunk. He was also worried about her health. He predicted that things would get worse once Christian left home, and he thought she would have a much better life if she left the bottle alone.

Christian added at this point that he had the same worry. He was afraid for his mother's health, and worried about what would happen between his parents once he was at the new school.

Betty said this was ridiculous. She never drank any strong alcohol. There was no alcohol problem at all.

I told the family that I did not intend to discuss whether Betty was or was not an alcoholic, or to take up what or how much she drank. What I would do with them was to try to find out how they could spend the time left with their last child before he moved from home: what they wanted in this period and hoped for in the future, and to consider what they had shared together over the years past. I told Albert and Christian that if Betty had an alcohol problem, it was her problem. They couldn't solve it for her. What they could do was to talk about their own concerns: what difficulties they saw for themselves and what resources they saw in the family. I subsequently saw them six times in all.

I proceeded from that point by asking each of them what they wanted. After what I had just said about Betty's drinking, it took them some minutes to reply to this question. Betty answered first. She wanted more attention and affection from Albert. Albert quickly retorted by saying that he wanted Betty to take better care of the house, and to be sober when he came home. Christian said he hoped he would do well in his final exams in the spring, and that he hoped he would find good friends at the new school, where he would begin in the autumn.

'It's good that you know what you want from each other,' I told them, 'but it is important, as Christian showed, to know what you want for yourselves, too.'

'I'm quite happy with what I have,' said the butcher.

Betty looked down at her hands, then replied without looking up. 'I have been thinking for some time that I would like to get some kind of job. But there are so many unemployed people about, that I'm sure I wouldn't have a chance.'

'And there's no need for you to work,' snapped the butcher. 'We have quite enough money without your working. You have work enough at home if only you'd do what needs to be done. If you did what you should in the house, you'd have more than work enough. And as far as wanting more attention, if you were sober more often, you'd get more affection from me.'

I could tell from the pained expression on Christian's face that he had seen this scene many times at home. This was exactly what he feared would escalate when he left his parents. 'Please,' he said, 'can't you stop arguing.'

'I'd guess that Christian is afraid you'll quarrel more when he is not with you,' I said, and the four of us sat quietly for some minutes.

Betty broke this silence by saying quietly but firmly, 'I am very tired of the quarrelling. I want to stop that part.'

'But do you think that I want to argue?' Albert unfolded his arms and leaned forward. 'I'm tired of arguing too.' I could tell from the way that his voice boomed that he really meant it.

'So,' I said. 'We have come to a point where all three of you agree. You know, it's very rare for people to come to an agreement so quickly in family therapy. Do you have any idea how rare it is to reach a point so quickly where a family agree?' They simultaneously sat back and up in their chairs, and all three looked amazed.

'Well,' said the butcher, clearing his throat loudly, '*shouldn't* families agree? Mine always did.'

I agreed with him. 'But you can see yourself how difficult it can be for families to agree. I want to ask each of you to think about something for next week. I want you to think about the things you disagree over in this family. And I want each of you — you, too, Christian — to think to yourself how you win disagreements.' With that task, I told them I would see them next week.

The next time we saw each other Albert said, 'I realize that I never lose disagreements.'

'How do you manage that?' I had opened the second family session — saying that whoever had learned something from doing the task could share it.

'It's quite simple. When I detect a disagreement beginning, I avoid the whole situation. It never pays to get too involved.'

'But you do get involved with people,' Betty said. 'I've seen you with your customers. They love it when you kid them, and argue with them and joke with them. I've seen how much they like you.'

'Of course they like me. But I'm tired when I come home, and then to find you slouched on the sofa, I'm not interested in anything else.'

'Tell me, Albert, how did you develop your strategy for avoiding situations and winning disagreements?'

'I can remember it quite clearly. It was when Grete,' he said, looking meaningfully at Betty, 'dropped our William.' He described how fond he had become of his eldest son's first girl-friend. How much he had enjoyed her company, how they'd take a beer together while she sat waiting for William to come home from work. When she decided to break off with William, it was as if she decided to drop Albert himself. It was at that point, he said, that he decided not to get too close to people any more.

'If that's the case, then it must be frightening for you to see your youngest son soon leaving home.'

Both he and Betty were visibly startled. 'It is for me,' Christian said.

We discussed how to use the time before Christian left for college. The things they mentioned wanting to do with one another were simple, but activities they genuinely wanted to share. Christian most of all wanted to take his mother to the cinema. Albert was surprised to learn that Christian had some interest in his own favourite hobby — billiards. Betty found it difficult to suggest anything at first. What she then said she wanted most, was to spend some quite cosy evenings with her two men at home. At first the two men showed resistance to this plan, but on further discussion they discovered that the two of them might prepare the menu and make it a special evening. One of Albert's dormant passions was cooking.

At the end of this session, I asked Christian and Albert to decide there and then which of their plans they would act on before I saw them next time. I turned to Betty. I instructed her to look at the jobs ads in the local newspaper in the coming week. She was not to make any decisions or telephone calls. Nor was she to even look at the ads when Albert was around, and certainly not to discuss them with him.

In the subsequent session, they evaluated what each family member believed he had gained from the others. Christian was clearest in what he felt he had gained from both his father and mother over his 16 years. Betty said that Christian was an affectionate and sensitive boy, and that Albert had been a good father and always a good provider, and everyone knew he was an excellent butcher. Albert said Betty had been a good mother. Even now she was able to make the grown-up children and their children feel at home when they returned on the weekends. He couldn't deny her that, he said.

One change that occurred was that Betty came to the fourth session wearing what was obviously a new blouse. I commented on it. She reacted with pleasure. She told me that over the past 20 years, she only had new clothes when her daughters bought them for her — at Christmas, birthdays, and so on. The blouse she wore was the first she had bought for herself since she had been married.

'It's a nice colour for you. And it's a new style, isn't it?'

'I like it too, Mother. I'm glad you bought it for yourself.'

Betty looked shyly at Albert, who said nothing. 'But you don't like it, do you?'

Albert sat up straight and responded as if on cue, 'I wouldn't exactly express it that way. If you didn't ask me, I wouldn't tell you I didn't like it. But since you asked, I have to say that it's not quite my taste.'

Later in that session, I told Betty I hoped she was still reading the jobs ads without discussing them. She had obviously done a fine job as a mother, and now as a grandmother without consulting Albert. There was no need to involve him at this stage of her life with new interests.

Once, as homework, I asked them to consider what they liked about themselves. Albert returned the following week without having done it. Before he was able to give any reason, I complimented him on his diligence. 'You know, it's usually the wives who don't do this task,' I told him. 'I think it's fantastic that you've created the opportunity for Betty to become more appreciative of her strengths.'

It was during this session that Betty mentioned that Christian had started to help her with some of her housework. But it was at the start of the next session that she entered my office glowing. It was impossible not to ask her what had happened.

'I started a new job today. I ran into the leader of the local play group yesterday at the supermarket. He was worked up because one of his assistants had to leave the playgroup suddenly — her own child was seriously sick. And John needed someone immediately to help out. It's only four hours a day, you know, but I offered my help anyway. And he took it! And it's a job! And they'll pay me! I started there today.'

'Well — but isn't that tiring, taking care of little children every day?' I was imagining what four hours with 3, 4 and 5-year-olds would mean for me.

Betty sat up in her chair and looked at me. She was a bit surprised by my comment. 'Do you think that little children can ever be tiring?'

The butcher cleared his throat. 'Well, I think you're right about that,' he said to me. 'But we'll see.'

The last time we met the session was a short one. Christian reported that he was now involved in the local swimming club. It had been too difficult to get to the cinema — which is in a larger town some miles away — so he had taken his mother for a swim at the new sports centre. And become involved in the evening activities after. He had tried billiards with his father, but he enjoyed the swimming much more.

'As we agreed to meet six times,' I said, 'I would like to spend this final session evaluating what we've done together.' The butcher answered first:

'I am very grateful that you have used your time with us. But I am an honest man, and I must admit that we still have the problems we came to you with. I can't see that there has been any change.'

Betty was still enjoying her new job but she too said that she still missed the attention and affection she had at one time received from Albert. She mentioned Christian's increased help with her housework, but she had to admit that she couldn't see that it had to do with the talks we had had together. 'I do feel better about myself,' she added finally. 'And I'm sure that has something to do with my coming here — though I'm not sure how it happened.'

Christian looked at me for a long time, then slowly said 'I don't know what more to say to you than thank you.' And looking at the butcher he added, 'And I disagree with you, Father.'

After a pause I looked at Albert: 'I'm glad you are brave enough to admit that you didn't get anything from treatment, and to be able to admit that not everybody was able to change. It's certainly allowed here to go on being the same person, and not to feel things in the same way as others.'

I ended by saying that they all knew, each of them, that if they needed help in the future, they could contact me. 'Yes,' concluded Betty, 'I would never again be afraid to ask for help.'

The 'Butcher's Family' typifies a kind of family which counsellors or social workers in community settings can meet. They have up to now functioned successfully, without government assistance or professional aid. They have seen their neighbours and acquaintances encounter problems which they could not solve. They are proud of their own accomplishments and the way in which they have lived. They tend to be inarticulate in the jargon of the 'helping professions', and the idea of change or therapy is foreign if not repugnant to them. They tend to resist elaborate interpretations or being coaxed to express their feelings. They won't be sold a problem they don't recognize. It can be argued that this kind of family actually loses more than it can gain from becoming a set of clients. And so a client status was not pressed on them.

The story demonstrates the value of the therapist confronting the reality of the problem that the family present (Minuchin and Fishman 1981). By redefining the major issues in terms of the effects of family transition for each of them, the therapist avoided legitimizing the family diagnosis, and crystallizing Betty's alcohol consumption as the primary problem. It furthermore prevents the therapist from falling into the trap of having to convince the patient of her disorder, and enables the therapist to concentrate on mobilizing the many resources within this family.

Children generally signal family trouble by becoming physically ill, or manifesting social or behavioural problems. Sometimes, as in Christian's case, they ask for help directly. I am reminded of one other case where a child requested assistance as explicitly as Christian. Janet was also due to move out of her parents' home in less than a year's time. She asked for help for herself rather than for her parents. Every time she tried to discuss her feelings about leaving or about the family, her father laughed at her. She asked if I would meet them all so she might talk with her parents before it was too late. The parents gained little in the session that ensued. But Janet and her younger brother opened a line of support and communication that continued after both of them left home.

The primary aim of the strategic therapist in this family was to prevent the repetition of the sequences in which the problem (Betty's drinking) has meaning or serves some purpose. All the tasks were formulated to alter such cycles. Picking up on the interests of the family members, the therapist sought to introduce, or prompt, complexity or alternative responses into the behaviour of family members or family subsystems. In simplest terms, this meant their doing different things (Fisch *et al.* 1982; Madanes 1981).

Within this conceptual framework, my goals were to raise Betty's self-esteem (cf. Satir 1967) and generate her involvement in some activities outside the home; to affirm and reinforce Albert's public image as good husband and father; to reorganize family hierarchy and responsibility so that Christian might leave home with fewer fears of resultant turmoil; and for all of them to experience that small changes from the present circumstances were possible.

I must add that although the plans this family devised for

entertainment eventually sounded like fun — cinema, food preparation, billiards — their planning session was no joy. A surprising number of families who seek help are simply not familiar with anticipating or planning enjoyable events together, or with seeing potential pleasure in everyday activities. In these sessions it takes considerable support and patience and positive reframing to help families formulate ideas that both stretch their expectations and imagination, and at the same time are realistic enough not to end in disappointment.

Notes

1   The recurrence of the paintbox here represents the therapist's willingness and ability to learn from experience with patients. Tom's task to purchase a paintbox (Chapter 2) aimed to redirect his attention from his insomnia to an interest he expressed in session: from the symptom to an alternative interest.

Tasks may certainly be used in this way, as part of an overall strategy, as well as for restructuring experiences, or for forcing new problem-solving behaviour. When the patient does not fulfil a task, it is often proof of an inappropriate or badly formulated task. A task, however, can be seen as a basis for choice. Either the patient follows the task or does not. He takes some action in either case.

In Tom's case, the therapist learned that some people with aspirations to create (painting, writing, etc.) or to engage in an activity out of the ordinary (often a sport, or some special hobby) have the plans, may even have the equipment, but rarely start. By prescribing the purchase of equipment for an activity the patient will most likely not pursue, and prescribing a restraint on pursuit of the activity ('not before they are absolutely ready') the therapist structures a success in an area previously experienced as failure to the patient.

2   This relationship between somatic manifestations, the attention they are given by the patient, and the consequences for the patient's experience of health or illness is clearly seen amongst high blood-pressure patients. It is generally accepted that high blood pressure is related to anxiety about social situations, personal demands, or general or specific worries. When an individual with a tendency to high blood pressure becomes anxious about, for example, giving a speech, his blood pressure rises. On recognizing the attendant symptoms, the patient may become more anxious and stressed for fear of more serious cardiac consequences, which can in turn contribute to the blood pressure level: a vicious cycle is generated.

An example shows how the therapist can influence this cycle, and influence the patient's experience and interpretation of his bodily signals.

One particular high blood pressure patient became, with increasing pressure at his work place, virtually obsessed with obtaining readings of his blood pressure levels. While patients in his category generally receive weekly or fortnightly checks, Hugo was ringing for appointments twice each week. The nurse and Hugo's GP agreed that his 'fixation' served to aggravate his condition. A strategy was conceived to ask him, before each check, to guess the level of his blood pressure, based on how well or poorly he felt that particular day.

If Hugo guessed his blood pressure was near normal, and the reading proved his guess wrong, the nurse joked that perhaps the clinic's equipment was faulty or of poor quality. When Hugo had a bad day, and his blood pressure matched, the congruence was interpreted as corroboration of improving bodily awareness and he was praised for increasing sensitivity to his feelings, reactions and milieu.

After a few weeks, Hugo himself was joking about the equipment and the quality of the nursing staff. He became more attendant to his body and his health, and at the same time more relaxed about obtaining the readings. He ceased his excessive demands for checks, and returned to the clinic's pattern of regular intervals between checks.

4 Crisis

Hans' Mother

Marion went to her doctor and asked for something to help calm her during the day, and to help her sleep at night. The doctor promised her a prescription, but he wanted her to come to see me as well.

The first time I met Marion it was a dark winter day. She brought little Hans with her and both were bundled against the damp Danish cold. Marion was not sure how I could help her. She told me that she had gone to the doctor because she was agitated during the day, and having a lot of trouble sleeping. She looked to me to be about 34 or 35. She had curly blonde hair and was pleasantly rounded in the way women her age can become. She was neither accusing nor demanding, but looked straight at me with her blue eyes from the start of our meeting. The dark circles under her eyes told me she had not slept for some nights.

After Hans had told me his name, I gave him a big sheet of paper and some crayons. 'Do you think you can make a fine drawing for my wall? You can see the others there? Or perhaps you can draw something so fine you'd like to give it to your father or mother. If you sit down on the floor here you can draw and listen to what we say. If you have something to say, you can join in.'

I told Marion that I didn't know if it would help her, but that she should tell me what was disturbing her and prevented her from sleeping. Marion told me that just over a year ago, Hans was diagnosed as having leukaemia. He received treatment for it, but it was still impossible to predict how long Hans would live, even though the prognosis was good. She and her husband were told they must keep an eye on Hans at all times. Any slight infection or normal childhood disease was much more dangerous for Hans than for normal children.

'Perhaps if we had other children this would be less of a tragedy . . . .' She and her husband had met as students at university. They married at graduation, and planned their careers and lives together. She and Eric had decided to have one child and to have that child late, so they would have the time to develop professionally, and then to take good care of their family.

Both worked as psychologists in separate institutions, and they hadn't any trouble arranging a part-time work schedule. That way they were able to share equally the care of their new baby. But following Hans' diagnosis, Marion had decided that she wanted to devote all her time to Hans. She quit her job, and Eric had taken up full-time work again.

That had been a year ago, but over the past six months, it had become more and more difficult for her to live with the knowledge that Hans might not live to be much older. The situation reached a point where it was now nearly impossible for her to talk with her little boy. Marion said she had the feeling that Hans knew what it was all about, and that made it doubly difficult for her.

I looked over at Hans, who was watching us from the paper where he was drawing something. He had his mother's bright blue eyes and round face. His hair was growing again following a course of chemotherapy, and I could see that it was the same as his mother's, perhaps a bit lighter in colour. I asked Hans if he wanted to join us. I asked what he was drawing. He didn't answer a single word. Having surveyed us, he went back to scratching on his paper with the crayons.

Marion continued her story. In this period it had also become impossible for her to talk with her husband about Hans' disease. She added that they never went out together any longer, because one of them always had to stay home with Hans. Marion didn't cry when she told the story. She looked as if she had shed all her tears long before. She stopped talking, as if there was nothing more she could say at that point.

I told her that I had three healthy grown-up children. I could only sympathize with her plight. 'Perhaps what I will tell you now will not mean anything to you at all. If that's the case, you should just forget it. But one time I was told that one of my children had a serious disease, and only a short time to live. For 24 hours, until a second doctor re-examined her, I had the same knowledge that you are living with constantly.

'My child was older then, 14, so I had had many good years together with her. No one told her anything, but my daughter knew exactly what was happening. Children are so alert and so sensitive, they always know what's going on from the way adults behave. She herself told me that she knew. At night I lay awake in my bed with the knowledge of her imminent death. I thought of all the happiness she had given me in the time I'd had her. I couldn't bear to think of a time when she would not be there. I forced myself to concentrate on thinking of what I wanted while I still had her with me. The next day we had a long talk together and she said to me: 'I don't think we should talk to Father about this now. It's much too hard for him.' During that day we planned and talked about what we wanted to do with the time we still had left. And the next night for me was different from the first.

'My child didn't die. The diagnosis was wrong. But since then I have always tried to use the time I have with her as if she could die tomorrow. The fact is that each of us could die any day.'

Marion peered at me, and it was as if her eyes and face came close up to me from a very great distance. I could see that Hans was watching his mother's face carefully. After a long silence, Marion said, 'I see what you mean. For a long time I have let other people take responsibility for my life with my child. From this day it will be different. From this day it will be Hans and I who decide what will happen.' With that, she stood up, raised her head high, and went to where Hans was drawing. She took his hand and said to me 'I don't know how it will be, but it's going to be *alive* from now on.'

I asked if she would come back with her husband, adding that she would know when the time was right. Hans left his drawing and took his mother's hand. Hans didn't look at me, only at his mother as she led him from the room.

When Marion rang two weeks later for an appointment for herself and her husband, I asked how things were. 'Very different,' she replied and she sounded as if she were smiling, at the other end of the line.

At one time I worked with a family which had adopted a refugee child. The boy insisted on coming through any doorway at the same moment as his new mother. Sometimes they managed to get stuck in the door and sometimes they didn't, but the effect when they finally entered was as something of a shotgun blast of humanity: teenager and mother tumbling into any room they blessed. When Eric joined Marion and Hans at the next session, all three of them managed to come successfully through my door at the same moment, all holding hands. They sat down with little Hans between them.

'When you rang me, Marion, you said things were very different. Could you tell me what's different?'

'When I left here and walked home with Hans, I began to think about what I was most fond of as a child. I remembered the mornings. I remembered when my father and brothers left, and I was alone with Mother. She always turned on the radio for a special musical programme and the two of us would sit together at the kitchen table and listen. Sometimes we crept together into the big bed, where she read me a story, or where we talked about what we had heard or about something we had done. I realized how much the feeling of peace at that time had meant to me. Nothing could hurry us. It was a time for just the two of us. A time we had just to ourselves.'

'So now we have changed our style at home, Hans and I. We don't hurry in the morning. Once we've sent Eric off, we do whatever we like. Sometimes we draw together. Sometimes we read stories or play cards. And sometimes we just lie quietly together in the big bed. I don't know why it wasn't difficult to change. It just felt natural. And even if I still know that Hans may not be with us for more than a year, it no longer takes all my thoughts and energy. Of course it is always with me, but what is more important now is that we enjoy the time we do have.'

'And in this short time, Hans has also changed. He enjoys our

48

mornings, but he also enjoys the time afterwards, when he is busy with his own things.'

Eric looked from Hans to Marion, and he added, 'Yes, and I think our relationship has changed.' With a gesture he showed that he meant the relationship between himself and his wife.

Marion smiled. 'Yet, that's right. We talk together much better now.' When they had gone to bed some days after seeing me, Marion told Eric how she was now spending her mornings with Hans. 'There is no point in talking about something we both know *will* happen, but cannot know when. We *can* talk about the time we have now and the time that's left.'

'I don't quite know what's happened,' Eric smiled almost to himself in a puzzled way. 'But over the last few months I was finding excuses to stay at work later and later. Sometimes I was almost afraid to come home. But just in this last week, I have looked forward to coming home to the two of you, in a way I haven't done for a long time.'

I let them know how impressed I was with what they had accomplished. Marion had looked upon her own past, and seen how her mother had given her peace and security. She had done the best thing any mother could do: to use that source of her security to give her own little Hans the sense of belonging and love he needed.

The sessions occurred three years before the time of writing. I have never seen this family since those two meetings, but I know from the doctors' conference that Hans is still alive, in a normal kindergarten, and leads the life of a normal child. Marion has taken up part-time work again. Marion and Eric still cannot know how long Hans will live, but they say if you didn't know, you couldn't tell from the way he looks and behaves that he is sick.

In the simplest sense, crisis can be defined as 'an upset in a steady state' (Rapoport 1965, p. 24, citing Gerald Caplan's formulation in seminars at the Harvard School of Public Health, 1959–60). This definition rests on the postulate that the individual develops manoeuvres and problem-solving activities to maintain personal and social equilibrium and to fulfil basic needs. Throughout the course of life these manoeuvres and activities adapt in response to discontinuities, emergencies or unexpected incidents. New solutions to life's general chaos and challenge are developed each day from the normal range of problem-solving mechanisms — which expands through life experience, maturation, cognitive input (reading, media exposure), and the like. In a state of crisis, however, usual problem-solving strategies do not suffice. By definition, then, crisis demands a solution which is new in relation to the individual's previous life experience (ibid.).

Given the disorientation and disorganization which predictably accompany crisis (Cullberg 1975), it is important for the therapist to discover which factors significantly contribute to the confusion, and which of these can be clarified or altered. Patients or their families receive — with terrifying regularity — conflicting or confusing information from the agents of their crisis: 'Your child is very susceptible. You have to take care that he does not come into contact with germs or diseases. And treat him as normally as possible.' Cancer patients are not unusually told their chances for full recovery are 50–50 — a useless if not malign 'fact'. Lise was informed she might be sterile, then later assured she would be able to conceive. Such data circumvent or confuse the problem-solving or survival mechanisms of the patient or parent.

Marion had responded to the received medical diagnosis in such a fashion that by the time she sought assistance, she was preoccupied with the eventuality of Hans' death rather than with what remained of his life.

Where patients appear to be incapacitated by such 'information', the therapist can assist the patient in sorting out conflicting messages, seeking additional information, and clarifying and redefining the situation so that the persons afflicted are better capable of activating their resources and experiences to deal with the crisis constructively.

While stress is principally regarded with a negative connotation, as having a pathogenic potential, the crisis state is considered to have 'growth-promoting potential'. In this light, crisis is perceived

> as a catalyst that disturbs old habits, evokes new responses, and becomes a major factor in charting new developments . . . a crisis is a call to new action; the challenge it provokes may bring forth new coping mechanisms which serve to strengthen the individual's adaptive capacity and thereby, in general, to raise his level of mental health (ibid., p. 23).

This suggests that people are capable of mobilizing their strengths in emergencies. By sharing my experience of a similar situation with Marion, I showed her crisis was not unique. My response was of a practical nature. It could not be medical or technical.

Marion's resources were her memories from her childhood and her ability to extrapolate from them. Even where patients have only bad or painful memories, they can draw from their experiences by defining how they would have liked it to have been — and therefore what they can create in their present circumstances.

Time is a crucial variable when the patient has received a terminal diagnosis. Given the limits of medical knowledge, it is also an unreliable one. The therapist has to acknowledge the predictable stages of physical and psychological shock which parents go through on receiving grave news about their child (Adler *et al.* 1975; Krant 1982; Maddison and Raphael 1975). She must also work to enable them to manage the subsequent material and emotional consequences. The period before death continues to be a time of life. While the family must prepare for an end that may be earlier than they could ever imagine, the remaining time can hold life and enjoyment and memories. This is to speak of a concept of sharing life amongst the whole family, so that all have lived together in the fullest way possible in the time that was left (Kubler-Ross 1978).

One client came to see me shortly after her mother died. She described how she and her sister had taken their mother out to their country home. My client's memories of this time were marked by sunlight coming through the leaves onto her mother's face. They had had a picnic in the forest, with champagne and strawberries. Her mother had been too weak to walk far, but they drove her out into a field, and carried her to a stream they all knew. The sisters let her feel the cold, fresh water on her bare feet. 'Of course,' she said, 'we talked a lot about our past together, but she also had to have a present which was alive.' It appears to be easy to forget that, even those near to death must have times of happiness, or seriousness, even nastiness — to engage with the present as well as to consider the past.

On one of my courses in crisis work, I met a woman with one arm. When I asked the group to share an experience of crisis, she described the time of her amputation. While she was still in hospital, her doctor, the nurses and the hospital social worker all came to her bedside. They all encouraged her to cry as much as she needed. She was not able to cry. She was completely numb. One day an elderly woman came to her bedside. She had read of the girl's accident in the local paper and wanted to visit her. The old woman had lost one of her arms in an accident many years before. She didn't pity the younger one. She told her it was time to start thinking of how good the arm she had left was, of what she would be able to do with that remaining arm. The old one related proudly that she now worked as chef in one of the better inns in the town. It was after she left that the young amputee cried. She realized in that moment how hard she would have to work to live life fully with just one arm.

This is a telling tale in that it shows that while the professional helper must want to help, and be available to help, he must also be prepared to accept that at times of crisis, people are extremely sensitive and may not actually be receptive to assistance. The persons concerned may be in shock, or feel self-protective against intrusion (Friedman *et al.* 1963; Janis 1973; Parkes 1981). The therapist has to be able to make way for those non-professionals who might be able to help, and to keep the door open to the time when the patient may welcome professional assistance.

Despite the content of Marion's interview in my office, I believe it was very important to keep Hans in the room. Removing children in these cases does not shield them from their parents' pain. They live with it each day. Excluding children also means the exclusion of information about the child's manner and about the parent–child

51

interaction. In most cases, small children are quite content with crayons and paper and a space on the floor.

The next case study is about a more grown-up boy who actually never had crayons at home, and very little space to be a child anywhere.

Alan

'Please ring Alan's mother — *urgent*!'

Late one afternoon when I returned from the clinic, I found the message that Alan's mother had telephoned and wanted me to call her back before 7. Alan's school had rung and demanded that she come and fetch him that day. She wanted to talk to me before she went.

Ruth was still in shock when she answered the telephone. Alan had attacked one of the school's young teachers — so badly that he had to be taken to hospital. Ruth wanted to know what to do when she arrived at the school. This was Alan's first physical assault on any person. I advised her simply to let him talk, as much as he wanted, and to try to be calm and kind to him. She wanted to know how soon I could see Alan, and I said he could come to Laegernes Hus at 9 the next morning.

Next morning at 8.30 I entered my office to find a pale young man seated there, his head hung down. Alan looked up at me, and then away very quickly. 'I've been a very bad boy,' he said in a low, husky voice.

We had all first heard of Alan at a clinic conference. One of the doctors described a boy who requested a home visit because he was sick. Alan, 14 at that time, met the doctor at his car, then gave him a tour of the family garden, saw him back to his car, and returned to the house. Another of the doctors recognized Alan's name and antics. Alan had consulted him more than once about the nail of his big toe, but there was never anything wrong with his foot. It was almost a year after this conference discussion that Ruth rang me for an appointment. The school was pressing the family to make him do something about his homework. While he attended school, Alan had done no school work for months.

Frank was 39. He and Ruth had been married 17 years, eight of which they had spent apart. A building constructor who could find work any time, anywhere, Frank had been a heavy drinker. It was known in the town that he beat his wife and their two small sons before she threw him out. He completely disappeared from the area, but when he returned eight years later, Ruth had taken him back into the home she had made with the boys.

As he cut down his drinking, Frank apparently cut down his violence as well — it was only Alan he had beaten since his return.

My first contact with Alan, then, came from this juncture where neither school nor parents could make him do his school work. I saw Alan with the whole family six times, and on one other occasion when his headmaster and teachers joined a session. For the purpose of this story, Alan's critical episode began at the 'efterschool'. The story illustrates the inability of adults to deal responsibly with a lad whose offences to date had been rather mild forms of misbehaviour and lack of involvement in school activities.

It is worth noting the normalcy of residential efterschools as an option for Danish students. Historically, residential schools were established to help young people whose education was interrupted by having to contribute to the family economy — helping out on the family farm, or in the family business. Living away from home for a period essentially freed young people from those responsibilities. It was an effort to raise the basic educational standard. Since the 1960s, efterschools have been perceived as an alternative for all pupils who would be seen to benefit from a year from their families in a new learning environment. It is thus regarded by Danes as a normal educational alternative. Efterschools do not carry a stigma of special education or treatment. There was probably more stigma attached when pupils originated in the poorer farming classes.

Alan's problematic behaviour at the school in Billund seemed enmeshed within the patterns of his parents and the school staff. A year at efterschool seemed to offer the opportunity for him to begin leaving home under normal, acceptable circumstances, and to gain the expected benefits of the efterschool experience: new teachers, subjects and mates, in new surroundings, with a fresh set of expectations of the pupils' potential. His parents concurred, and the last two sessions were spent planning for Alan's departure.

When Alan came home from efterschool at Christmas, he called at the clinic to say hello. He looked pleased to be back, but refused to tell anything about the school itself. 'It was going OK' was the most he would say. During this vacation, Ruth rang me three times. Each time she was nearly hysterical, weeping and complaining that she couldn't cope with having Alan at home. I offered to meet them at the clinic or at their home, but she refused. Relatives were visiting from other parts of the country for the holiday season. She couldn't dream of family therapy then. Alan visited me once more before returning to school. He had never liked any kind of sport. In his short time at the residential school he had grown much taller, but also softer and flabbier. At the end of this Christmas vacation, he looked unhappy and weary as well.

That was the last I saw of him before the telephone call in May. And now he was sitting in my office, his head hanging on his chest, his face very pale. I asked him if he would tell me about what happened at school. 'No, I won't tell it anymore. It's true what they told you, but I can't talk about it anymore.'

I asked him what had happened afterwards. He said he'd wanted to apologize, but that they kept him by himself in an office. They would not let him see the teacher before he was taken to hospital. I asked if the school threw him out. He didn't think so. No one had told him he couldn't come back. They just said something about staying away for a week or so. I guessed they would let him return to sit exams at the end of the month.

'But I won't go back there any more. I can't look them in the eyes ever again.' I asked what he would do, and he said that he just wanted to forget: 'But it's with me all the time.'

This time his parents agreed to come for a family session. They came the very next day. All four of them trudged into my office and sat down. They were used to my office from previous sessions, but this time the parents sat down with Alan between the two of them. He had always sat on the perimeter of the family circle before. I looked silently around at the faces. As soon as my eyes met those of Mark — Alan's older brother by a year — he blurted out: 'He didn't beat him up this time! I'm so glad he didn't beat him up this time!' My gaze passed from Mark to Frank. His voice was so low I almost missed what he said:

'I won't hit him any more. I told him that he'd been beaten for the last time.'

I talked with the family about the consequences of what had happened for all of them as well as for Alan. I asked if they knew whether the school was going to press charges. They had been assured that neither the school nor the teacher would press charges. But Alan adamantly refused to return for the final examinations. He was determined that he would never return to the school again. And Frank agreed with him: 'If that school is the kind of place where this kind of thing can happen, I don't want him back there. I won't under any circumstances allow my boy to go back there.'

The family discussed the time that Alan had spent away from home. My particular concern was the foreseeable difficulties his return would trigger. His parents and brother spoke at length of new plans and hopes for Alan's return. I tried to get them to discuss the difficulties that were sure to occur, and ways they might avert or deal with them as they arose.

This session was a crucial one in Alan's story. Had the family been capable of following through a tidy scheme of evaluation of gains, aspirations and plans for the future, he might have been able to live at home and return to his original school. Assessing the realistic possibilities of this, however, I began to investigate alternatives for Alan's future. In this session I began to teach Alan to consider the consequences of his actions. He repeated that he couldn't do that any more. I instructed him to go home, to think over once again what he had done, and to return the next morning. I also told Alan that from the next day, he was to begin a programme of running and cycling. He did follow through on this demand, but I'm sure he persevered because of his relationship to me rather than from any personal motivation.

When I saw him the next morning, I asked him what he wanted to do. He didn't know; what he did know was that he would not return to the efterschool. I looked at him hard: I told him that if his life didn't change at this point, there would be only one way for him. He had already taken more than one step in the direction where you find friends who are as afraid as you are, where you get life and excitement from doing destructive, hurtful things, and where you end by being a criminal.

It became clear at that point that Alan needed three things and he needed them quickly. I began to look for a place for Alan: one which would be a family strong and open enough to accept him as a member, where the father worked from home so that Alan could work together with him — to learn that work has to be done properly and finished even if it is boring — and where there was a job that would keep him meaningfully occupied. At 16 Alan had to catch up in learning what neither his family nor any school had succeeded in teaching him.

I knew of a dairy farm several miles from Billund. I knew the farmer there and that he had the qualities to be a good model for Alan. Paul was a man in his late thirties, warm and strong in body as well as in mind. He combined his hard-working nature with a capability to feel things deeply and express his feelings honestly. I knew his wife Helen wouldn't be overinvolved with Alan, wouldn't try to be a mother to him. She would be able to give him warmth and comfort and make him feel welcome. Both were involved in the dairy farm. Both worked at home every day.

I went to the family and asked if they would help. After a short deliberation they said 'Yes'. Then I told Alan about the plan. I told him it was the only thing I could suggest for him. I believed that he would be able to learn there what he needed to live a good life. Ruth, Frank and Alan visited Paul and Helen one evening, and the day after — just two weeks after the incident at the school — Alan started working on the farm.

The farm was too far for Alan to commute each day, so he moved in with the family. Paul and Helen had two small children — little girls of 8 and 10 — and there was another farm-hand, a lad of 19 who also lived with the family. When I visited them after a month, Helen and Paul informed me how much Alan liked playing with the little girls, and going for walks with the big family dog. 'He still can't finish what he starts,' said Paul. 'He's not yet worth the pocket-money I give him.'

In August Ruth invited Alan to spend his three-week summer holiday with them. Even in that short time she rang me twice for advice, and she rang Helen once that I heard of. Frank was satisfied that Alan had not returned to the efterschool, and that he had a steady job. In Denmark youths can legally stop school at 14, if they have guaranteed full employment. Frank saw no need for the family to return for help ever again.

Alan came to see me once during this August holiday. The exercise and hard work at the farm were obviously benefiting his body. The jelly-like flab was gone, and his body was taking on a firmness more appropriate for a healthy 16 year old. He stood straighter, but his dark-green eyes were sad. Despite the family's dramatic history of Frank's disappearance, and rumours that Mark and Alan were beaten by Ruth's lover as well as by Frank, Alan always showed great loyalty to his family. Once when I asked him what was important to him, he told me that he loved his mother more than anything else. 'I don't know what I'd do if she died,' he had said then. 'I think I couldn't go on living.'

I knew that Alan had not yet reached a point where he felt he had a place for himself: a place where people really wanted him, a place to which he belonged. From the way he looked and behaved, though, one could see that he was on his way to more realistic expectations of himself and of relationships. I couldn't help smiling when I watched him leave the clinic. He had acquired a way of putting his right hand in his back pocket as he strolled down the corridor and out the door — just as Paul was in the habit of doing. It was the first indication I had ever seen that Alan had found himself a significant male model.

'If he goes on in the way he is now,' Paul told me when I drove out to the farm at the end of September, 'it won't be long before he's able to earn a normal wage.' Neither Paul nor Helen were sure exactly what happened during the August vacation, but they could see that Alan had changed. 'His work still isn't perfect, but I know if I ask him to do something, he'll work till he finishes it. Even if it takes a long time.'

At the end of my visit, I joined the family for coffee. While I continued to chat with Paul and Helen, Alan prepared the little girls to go out for a walk. They all put on their coats, and he took each of them by the hand. Going towards the door, he called in a low voice, 'Besssss!' The golden retriever looked up a little puzzled, then raised herself sleepily to join them. Only Paul ever called to her in that deep voice.

It is understandable when workers and teachers become frightened and impatient in this kind of situation. In the first place, it's an example of a crisis that the key individual precipitates as a consequence of his own actions. Secondly, the critical event here admitted enormous uncertainty about prospects for Alan's adult life. He might well have been sent to a correctional institution (the legal age for criminal prosecution in Denmark is 15). As it was, he was subjected to full psychiatric evaluation after the incident.

To follow through a crisis like Alan's creatively, so there can be a constructive outcome, the therapist must demonstrate the belief that all events can have substantial significance in a person's life. My experience in the field suggests to me that a number of professionals regard crisis as an explosion, from which little can be salvaged, and to which institutionalization provides an orderly answer. There must be some value or belief that the individual can come through a crisis enriched, with increased possibilities. Putting this belief into operation is the professionals' challenge.

Roget's Thesaurus (1963) categorizes 'crisis, emergency, [and] timeliness, opportunity, opening' under the same rubric. The implications of this are significant to the professional. Getting the client to articulate feelings or reactions is clearly not enough in this case. The therapist must make the most of the opportunities which crisis presents by seeking to utilize the available resources in the individual, in the family and in the community.

Particularly where a crisis is the consequence of an individual's actions — and these actions can be directed and malicious, as in Alan's case, or unintended, as an athletic woman whose activity provokes a miscarriage — it provides the point for the patient to cease denying the factors that precipitated the crisis. The job of the therapist is to help the person face the activities leading to the crisis and its onset, and to evaluate in which ways he has contributed to it. This is no easy therapeutic task, for it means blending techniques of realistic evaluation and confrontation, while avoiding reproach or blame. Alan's 'I only want to forget it' is as characteristic of middle-age professionals, as it is of 16 year olds at times of crisis. But the question of responsibility and accountability is especially important for individuals such as Alan. In cases where adolescents are on the brink of delinquency, the establishment of ego identity, questioning and integrating personal values, and learning appropriate social behaviour are essential (Erikson 1950; Glasser 1965; Miller 1965).

This case study might go into a chapter entitled 'The limits of family therapy'. When Ruth first telephoned me I was able to see the family nine times. Neither Alan's parents, nor the teachers whom I called in for a special meeting about his problems at school were able to follow through responsibly on verbal commitments to help Alan with his school work. And Alan, of course, put up every obstacle to their assistance. For example, one day he stole his maths teacher's hat and wore it jauntily throughout the class. His classmates loved it, but the teacher was already so fed up with him that he threw him out of the room at the end of class. He forgot all about Alan's homework and the agreement to go through it with him.

One seemingly positive consequence of family therapy was that each of the family members was determined to concentrate on their own activities: pursuing their special interests or hobbies. This worked fine for the parents and older brother, who all had other interests and other friends. But Alan hurried home from school each day, as he had since he started school. He had no special friends or positive contact with teachers. In some ways, this development heightened his isolation and 'differentness' in his family.

Following the episode at the efterschool, I worked with them so that they could prepare for Alan to leave home in the most normal way possible, with some future to look forward to. Both Alan's age and some of the patterns I discerned in the early session helped determine my efforts to place him with another family. While 16 is not young, Alan was enough of a child by my calculation to need to develop his personal identity and self-worth, and to learn to behave responsibly. At home, Alan was the boy who would be criticized for cleaning the floor badly, given a hiding for talking back, then allowed to run off with the knowledge that someone else would clean where he had swept. Once I recognized the limits of family work in supporting the development he needed, I began to focus on Alan as an individual — while remaining available to the rest of the family (Montalvo and Haley 1981).

In retrospect, one can always question the placement of the boy following the efterschool incident. Although the farm provided a positive alternative and direction for this young man, I cannot help but wonder whether I should have worked more intensively in supporting his parents to move him out. With the intervention described, Alan was removed from his home, and still remained a part of its dynamics in a way which might not have been the case had his parents taken the initiative in having him find a place in the world as a responsible adult, if they had sent him positively from their home (Haley 1980). Still, Alan's experience on the farm has equipped him well for adult life. He has continued his education, travelled abroad, and today leads an active life in the little community.

Despite his lack of interest in school, Alan was an intelligent youth quick to learn what he wanted to learn — as is the case with most young people.

In the story which follows can be shown the importance of hearing simple messages, in order to help lead a client through a crisis time — away from further institutionalization and into new discoveries about life.

Else's Husband
The details of Else's story are special, but the essence of her tale resembles that of very many other women.

Else is 53. Her husband Ed is 56, and they have been married 27 years. Else used to be a factory worker, and she took up work again after a lengthy break. For a period of nine years in between, she cared for Ed's father. Else would never openly admit it, but the work she did at home in those years paid for the house she and Ed inherited on the old man's death.

Ed's family had all been farmers. When his mother died, Ed's father was too old and too weak to carry on the farm alone. In fact Ed hated farm work, but his father had never fully accepted that he would not take over the farm. Having no other sons, the old man expected to live with him and his family in his late years. Ed and Else could barely afford the small rented flat where the space for their two children was so restricted, so moving into the fine, big house the five would share together was a fantastic opportunity. The unspoken condition of this arrangement was that Ed's father would be taken care of in his final years.

Else soon found that this meant giving up her job in the factory where she and Ed worked, in order to work full time at home. In many ways these were good years. For the first time the children — John was 12 and Jane 10 at that time — were able to have their own bedrooms. Else and Ed enjoyed taking care of the big garden together, and Else discovered there were many things about being a housewife that were pleasurable. She had worked in a factory from the time she left school, so being able to take good time to do the housework was quite an experience for her.

No matter how hard she tried to take good care of Ed's father, he complained about having to leave his beloved farm. The old man never said it outright, but he always framed his complaints so that Else could hear he felt she had taken Ed away.

Jane moved out of the house to live with a boy-friend as soon as she finished school. John was a student in another part of the country. So Else was basically alone in taking care of the old man in his last year — a long year of illness, pain and bitterness. Else felt Ed was so occupied with his job and the big house and garden, that she never involved him with her troubles with his father.

During this last year, and at the time of his death, Else believed she was doing the right thing in following the wishes of the old man. Ed's sisters did not hide their belief that he ought to be admitted to hospital for proper treatment. But the old man insisted on staying at home and dying in his own bed.

In the first year after the death, Else felt very tired. After rearranging the house to make it into her and Ed's home (Ed's father had had firm ideas about how he wanted his home to look), she decided it was time to go back to work. They had lost the benefit of the old man's pension after his death, and both she and Ed agreed they could use the extra income. When she had left the factory, they told her that she would always be welcome back, so there was no difficulty in obtaining her old job. That was four years ago.

She telephoned me because one of the GPs told her that perhaps I might help her. After our first session together, I realized I could not recall the colour of Else's eyes, or the colour of her hair, or much about how her body looked. I did remember clearly the expression on her face. There were strong lines about her eyes and mouth. In the set of that mouth, you could see how hard her life had been. Else, too, had a special way when she thought about something very deeply, of closing her eyes and drawing in her upper lip. After a moment she would open her eyes and raise her head to answer. Her voice was a trifle shaky, but she answered my questions as clearly as possible. She was the woman who would take whatever life offered and do her best to see it through to the end.

At our first session she apologized for having such difficulties in forgetting the past. She could not stop blaming herself for what she had done in the past. I asked her to tell me about her past, and she related the story above.

Else had been admitted to a psychiatric hospital two years before our meeting. She had forgotten the diagnosis, but remembered they had given her all the treatments — shock treatment, of course, included. I asked her what had happened in the years between her father-in-law's death, and the time she went to hospital. Then she told me the story of her daughter.

Jane married shortly after her grandfather died. Curt owned a curiosity shop. He was 29 at the time of the marriage and Jane was 18. He was very hard-working and an honest fellow, so neither Else nor Ed had worried when Jane first moved in with him. Else valued Curt's earnest trustworthiness so much, she said she couldn't have found a better husband for her daughter herself. He gave her the feeling of having a son again. She had missed John since he had moved so far from home.

When Jane's baby was born, Else was ready for a grandchild. She was much aggrieved when they brought the baby home with the news that he might be epileptic. The hospital couldn't say for sure, but to prevent a mishap, the parents were given drugs and instructions to keep a careful eye on him. They had to bring him to the hospital each month for a check-up.

Else loved her little grandchild. At least twice each week, she visited her daughter to help out as she could. She took pains not to interfere in the way her daughter handled the baby, but she did notice that Curt was looking poorly. At first she thought it was the stress of the situation, along with the demands of his work — with Jane not helping out in the shop any longer. She was sure each time she saw him, though, that Curt looked worse. He was losing weight fast and he looked very pale. She tried to talk to them about it, but they rebuffed her concerns. Jane admitted that her husband was tired. But she could not persuade him to see the doctor, and she was so occupied with the baby, she decided it was nothing to worry about.

One day when Else came to visit, she found Curt propped up in a chair in the living-room. Jane had gone shopping, and when she discovered Curt he was so weak that he was almost unconscious. The baby lay crying in his cot. Else rang for an ambulance immediately and Curt was rushed to hospital. Examination showed that he had a kidney ailment, and he spent some weeks in hospital before he was able to return home.

All the time that Curt was in hospital, Else was haunted with the fear that she had interfered. She tried to talk about this with the two of them, and with Ed. All tried to assure her that she had done the right thing. But Else could only believe that she had interfered when she had no right to. I told her I understood that it must have felt as if she took responsibility for many other people. It was quite natural in that case to worry about whether she had done the right thing.

I instructed Else to go home and to concentrate on thinking about what she might have done differently. She should consider all the possible alternatives both with the son-in-law and Ed's father. I said it was important that she herself evaluate what she had done rather than letting others tell her that what she had done was right. I asked her to come back next week and tell me the results of her thinking.

When Else returned, she told me that it took her only a few hours to reach her conclusion. If she were faced with the same situations today, she would do all the same things again. As soon as she saw that, she realized that she had to leave the past behind her.

After that she said she began thinking about her job. She realized how tired she had been at the time of her first breakdown. She had had to persuade herself to go to work. And the same thing happened last week, when her colleagues carried her from the factory where she had collapsed onto the floor, to the clinic. Again, she had had to persuade herself to go to work, and to struggle to get through the housework. She had gone on until she dropped, both times.

I asked Else if she would bring her husband with her next time. She said they had discussed his coming in the week since I had seen her, and they had agreed it was a good idea. Since she had collapsed at work the week before, Else needed help at home. And in the way she described it, I could hear that she was quite amazed that Ed had begun helping out as much as he did.

Else complained eloquently about the discomfort the menopause had brought her. She was unable to sleep at night because of cramps in her legs. She had cold sweats accompanied by painful needle-like tingling. She spent much of each night pacing the floor, and had done so for the past four years. She had some hormone pills from her doctor. And a few of the older women at work told her not to worry: those kinds of symptoms could last for ten years, and then they would gradually fade. I asked if she also had cold sweats when she was at work, or when she went to her whist club, one of her great enjoyments. She closed her eyes, and drew in her upper lip. When Else opened her eyes and looked at me, she said that, remarkably, the pain was absent at work or at the club.

I told her it was important that she gain more time for herself, and for the things she wanted to do. I suggested she make a contract with her husband about the work at home. She said they had discussed it once, but there wasn't any agreement.

61

In the third session, Else described her recent visit to Jane and Curt. They were doing better, and the baby was growing more and more beautiful each week. She and Ed had made some division of the housework. Both wanted the garden, but for once in her life, Else held out for what she wanted, and had the privilege of caring for the garden she loved so much. While she was working in the garden, she heard a voice calling, and when she looked up, the new neighbour was beckoning to her.

Else had seen the removal van, but not yet met her neighbour. She was gathering berries and, calling to Else, asked whether she wanted a taste — they were so delicious. The conversation ended by the two of them taking coffee in Ursula's kitchen. Ursula had been a widow for years. When she retired from her managerial position with the Post Office in Copenhagen, she decided to buy a small house and move closer to her only son and grandchildren. Else wasn't sure how it started, but over the past week, she and Ursula began daily walks together. During one of these walks, Ursula told her that since she started doing yoga, she had to take a walk every day. The yoga made her feel more in balance, and more aware of nature and of her body in a very positive way. In spite of Else's pain in her legs, she admired Ursula so much that she determined to accompany her each day from then on.

She was still having cold sweats at night, Else informed me before I could ask. But she didn't have the leg cramps any more; she was no longer pacing at night. She had, of course, begun doing yoga with Ursula, and their walks each day grew longer and longer. Else felt so full of gratitude, she felt she had to express it to Ursula. Oddly enough, at the same time, Ursula had brought her a gift: a fine pair of running shoes. She insisted Else had to take good care of her feet.

I sat back in my chair and looked at this woman I had met four weeks before. I thought about how different she looked from the first time I saw her. The downward pull that the tightness of her mouth had caused was gone, and her face was more open. I would have trouble describing it exactly, but in a very subtle way she held her head differently. All this from a pair of running shoes? Else interrupted my thought with a description of her own meditations over the past week. Since her collapse she had been on sick leave from the factory. As the time grew nearer to return, she was doubting whether she wanted to remain a factory worker for the rest of her life. She was discovering there were other ways to spend her time. We talked a lot about how important it was not to stop learning, or doing new things at her age. She found Ursula such an inspiring companion. It was then I heard for the first time that Ursula was 70! Once more we ended the session planning an appointment where she would come together with her husband.

When the time came, Else rang and said she didn't want to take up my time. Besides, since she started back at work again, she found herself pressed for time for her walks and the yoga. I wondered how her thoughts about the future had gone, and she told me that she had signed up for 'Expeditions in Nature — an educational exploration of flora and fauna' in the area. She was a bit nervous about whether the others on the course would have more knowledge than she, but I could hear in her voice that she was excited, and pleased as well.

She felt she had benefited so much from thinking about the future that she said she wanted to bring her busband along to the next session to discuss their future together. We ended our conversation with a date for a new appointment.

Else came alone the next time. She complained about her sweating, and a new symptom, headaches. There was no longer a question of waking up in the night. These headaches were so draining, she found she needed more sleep than ever before. She spoke as if somehow the headaches had something to do with me. It was clear that she was afraid of ending up as she had before, of breaking down before she realized that she was overloading herself. I suggested that her headaches were a signal from her body that she had taken on more than she could carry. Perhaps it would be wise to reconsider the best use of her time and energy. I suggested she telephone me when she had something new to tell.

I didn't hear from Else for some weeks. Then she rang to report that she had a new job. She heard there was an opening at the garden nursery in her neighbourhood. The work was hard, but she hadn't been afraid of that, and they had given her such a good recommendation from the factory, she won the job over 29 applicants! I asked how she was feeling. The headaches had stopped as soon as she had obtained her new job. Her cold sweats still came in the night, but she was able to cope with them now. There was so much to learn about the plants at the nursery. When she awoke in the night, she turned on the light and read one of the books about plants that she borrowed from the library until she fell asleep again. I asked after Ursula, who was fine. And now Else had something to teach Ursula. She was learning more about plants from her new job than she ever dreamed she would know.

I expressed my regrets at not meeting her husband. Else replied that she had always been 'too easy' listening to other people. She said that Ed really wanted to join her, but this time she felt it was something she should discover and work out alone. That was why *she* had decided not to bring him.

Else took care of others throughout her life. She nursed Ed's father for years with virtually no help. She carried the burden of his physical ailments, and assorted complaints and criticisms without troubling anyone. Both of her breakdowns followed periods of hard work and the stress resulting from her participation in other people's lives at times of great need. The notion that work is important and necessary to live a good life was fundamental to Else, as to many of her generation. For Else the result was that her overcommitment of time, energy and personality to her work life left her vulnerable physically and psychologically. The contemporary conventional response to consequent stress symptoms are medication, hospitalization and other forms of treatment which put individuals back on their feet without developing means for avoiding relapse.

Else's circumstances are in no way unique: 16.6 per cent of the Danish population are women over the age of 50.[1] A substantial population of women spend their lives serving the needs of others, or letting their jobs take the biggest place in their lives. Identity, life patterns and bases for meaningful purpose are well established by this age. Yet this stage of the life-cycle presents physiological, social and psychological changes that are regarded by some specialists as the greatest stress on the human organism: 'when age and time begin their demand for self assessment and reappraisal' (Cath 1965, p. 181).

Assessment of the life one has lived involves reception and perception of feedback, both of which play a role in determining self-image all through life (that is, whether or not the individual sees himself as worthwhile). These factors gain prominence in middle and later years. The ways in which social information is perceived creates a feedback loop whereby denial of failure, limitations or successes, or a sense of bitterness or regret colour the individual's experience of the present.

The implications, then, of professional treatment for the symptoms presented by patients like Else are serious indeed. At the time of Else's disease, her personal network of peers encouraged complaisance and tolerance of discomfort, her family offered empty assurances, and her previous breakdown provoked an institutionalization which did not prevent a subsequent repetition of her pattern, or the resultant physical collapse. Else's story demonstrates counselling which encourages the patient to appreciate the events of early life and to plan a fruitful present and future.

The basic objectives of my work with this woman was to shift the responsibility for Else *to* Else, to consistently support that shift in any form it took, and to stimulate and encourage the enrichment of her present activities and her future. The first step was to ask Else to evaluate past actions with regard to her father-in-law and her son-in-law. This was to accelerate the activity in which she was already much involved. Her, perhaps surprisingly, efficient use of that task reinforces the principle of brevity in brief intervention. From that point Else began to consider her job and the way in which she lived.

Persistent and continuing reinforcement of the healthy reactions of the patient are vital. I supported her renegotiation with Ed over household tasks, and their life at home, and consistently acquiesced to her refusal to bring Ed with her. Early family therapy literature stresses the necessity of seeing spouses conjointly. Accepting Else's 'resistance' was a strategic recognition of her decision to handle this crisis on her own terms. A positive self-image enhances the individual's capacity to deal with the loss and depletions which accompany the aging process (Cath 1965). In considering the importance of raising an individual's self-esteem, it can be difficult to judge how the positive responses of a professional related to any client's new ventures. Else told me that her relationship with Ursula was the first real friendship of her own for many, many years.

Basic characteristics of my work with Else and similar cases include:

1   *clarification* — to elicit from the patient a concrete description of the crisis. In what ways is the episode a crisis for the patient? What were the events which led up to the crisis? How did it come about?
2   *reframing* — putting the event into context as a logical response to the life the patient has lived, and relating it to other events which have occurred in the course of the patient's life.
3   *evaluation* — what were the patient's activities and patterns before, during and following crises in the past. How did she manage during the course of the current crisis? What were the alternatives? How would she have handled it differently?
4   *planning for the future* — crisis is an event from which an individual never emerges quite the same as when they entered. The answer to 'what happens next?' depends to some extent on the nature of the crisis — as the young woman with one arm told. She realized the significance of her amputation when she understood how hard she would have to struggle to lead an ordinary life.

Preparing for what will follow marks a final stage of crisis management. This involves goal setting, and possible redirection of aims or activities in the patient's life (Keleman 1974; Krantzler 1975). Crisis provides the opportunity for the individual to learn from past and present experience, and to exercise personal resources to a fuller capacity. Therefore, endorsing Else's trust of herself and development of her self-esteem and responsibility helped Else *use* her crisis as a point from which to evaluate the way in which she was living and had lived: in order to 'take charge' of her life to the point where she could fashion a better quality of life, and prevent further relapse.

Else transformed before my eyes, and I shall never know how, or what part I as therapist played in her development.

Note
1   According to the Danish Bureau of Statistics (Danmarks Statistick) the population of Denmark on 1 January 1983 was 5,116,464, out of which women totalled 2,595,244, of whom 854,633 were over 50.

5   Responsibility

Susanne and Victor

The woman who came into my office had not one single hair out of place. She was impeccably dressed. But she trembled all over and her eyes were unhappy, and she looked as if she had been crying for a very long time. Susanne said she had been waiting a long time for her appointment with me. So long, in fact, that she requested admission to a psychiatric hospital in the interim. Her GP refused to comply with this request.

Susanne first visited her GP over a month before this meeting, because of severe stomach pains. At the same time she started having what she called anxiety symptoms. She was sure, for example, that at times her heart skipped beats. She started awake in the night, convinced that her husband had stopped breathing. Sometimes she rang him at work because she was afraid of being at home alone. She had cried so much in the doctor's office that the doctor insisted she stay home on sick leave. And all these symptoms had intensified up to the time of our first meeting.

I asked her to tell me what had been happening in the period just before the stomach and anxiety symptoms began. She said she wasn't quite sure where the story began, but she would try to tell it. Susanne was the only woman employed as sales-person for a large local medical firm. Her job included accompanying customers on tours of the firm so they could see how the apparatus they would buy was made and used; taking customers to business meals, and occasionally arranging conferences for potential buyers. While her male colleagues had secretaries to help with the details of entertaining and arranging, it appeared that Susanne was assumed capable of organizing and executing all her own affairs.

She was also the person at home who took charge of cooking, shopping and all the cleaning. She expressed pride in their home. She was satisfied with the life-style she had with her husband, and could not understand it when she started feeling run down and stressed. She noticed that something was wrong when she found herself not wanting to do anything. She had to force herself to get out of bed in the morning. She lost her sense of humour, and she started feeling bored at the parties she and Victor used to enjoy so much. Then there was the panic that seized her — which she could neither anticipate nor protect herself from.

She was disappointed that neither her parents, nor her sister or brother, nor any of her friends understood her. Whenever she tried to describe her experiences to close family or friends, they replied that she had to pull herself together. 'If I could have done that,' she said, 'I wouldn't have needed to talk to anybody. I've always been able to pull myself together before. These symptoms are so frightening because they're just not me. How long is it going to go on like this!?'

I said I did not know how long her discomfort would last. But in the first place, if she felt like staying in bed, she should do it. She was on sick leave, after all. It often turned out that when patients manifest the kinds of symptoms she had, their bodies were providing a warning or opportunity to take stock of what was going on in their lives. The time their symptoms demanded allowed for reflection on how closely their lives focused on what was important to them.

Our first session was a brief one. The next time she was to return with her husband. He was sure to play a significant role in whatever process she would have to go through to bring this uncomfortable episode in her life to its close.

Victor was probably the most attractive man who ever entered my office. He remarkably resembled Cary Grant, but where C.G. merely has brown eyes, Victor's were a smoky grey. He was gentlemanly and genuine in his manner, seeing that Susanne was comfortably arranged, and taking care to shake my hand and introduce himself. I asked in what ways he was affected by his wife's depression – the word she used to describe her state. I smiled to myself as I imagined Susanne waking this man in the middle of the night to make sure he was alive and breathing.

'Of course it influences my life. I cannot forget that she is staying home feeling so bad. I get rather frightened and nervous when she calls me at work. I never know what to say or do for her. I have tried to explain Susanne's calls to my staff. You know, she calls me at work at least three times a week. I am a chemist, and sometimes I must serve or advise customers in my shop. My assistants have to call me to the 'phone nearly every time she rings. All of them know her. They can't believe that things could get Susanne down so seriously.'

How did he see the beginning?

'Susanne and I have been married for seven years. We met at a conference where she was presenting a new treatment apparatus. People always make jokes about conferences and affairs. I had always kept away from them. I was 41 then, and not married. Frankly, up to then, I had never felt like being married. I enjoyed life as I had it. But when I saw Susanne, my mind was changed.

'She had to make much bigger changes. At that time, Susanne was married to her first husband. She had been married ten years, and had three children by him. She had always been faithful to her husband. She had a very strong conviction that faithfulness was an important part of marriage. But even if we both felt it was wrong, and it was something we had never thought of doing before, what happened between us was something neither of us could resist.'

'I thought I was happy with my first husband, but I never really understood how it was to be loved and to love for everything you thought or felt or did. I thought if I made a clean break with my first husband, he would be able to find another woman who really loved him and who could become a mother to our children. I decided if I never saw any of them again, there would not be any competition between their new mother and me. They would consider her as their real mother. I moved with Victor to this part of the country one month after we met, and I've seen neither my husband nor my children ever since.'

'But to go back to your question about how it began. I think I saw the start of Susanne's depression that evening before the big exhibition. When you came home late, and went to bed in tears, and cried throughout the night.

'You see, Susanne is the only woman with her position and responsibility in her firm. There really aren't any assistants for the work that has to be done in entertaining customers or setting up exhibitions and the like. But the salesmen use the secretaries for a lot of the detailed work. Susanne has always refused to do that. She's always seen to all the final points herself. She wouldn't dream of asking anybody for help, or troubling them with what she felt was her responsibility.

'This particular day was the eve of the firm's major yearly exhibition. She stayed on after all the others had left to complete preparation for the programme. I'm still not sure what happened there, but she came home very late. She sank into a chair and I actually had to help her to bed. She hasn't been the same since.'

It was near the end of the session, so I asked them if they were willing to try what I would ask them. They agreed. I hesitated — told them it wouldn't be too easy. But they insisted they were willing to try whatever I thought would help.

'A part of what's wrong now is that you have always done everything perfectly, Susanne. And now we can see the results. You can see that you can't get further from being perfect. In this next week, I want you to do ten things wrong each day. I want you to do these ten things consciously wrong. Mistakes don't count. I want you to be as painstakingly wrong as you do other things painstakingly right. Can you do that? Fine.

'Victor. Your task is simpler. I simply want you to ring Susanne each day — twice each day. She's still home on sick leave, so I want you to 'phone her each morning and each afternoon from work to see how she is faring.'

Asking people to make mistakes or do things badly is really too much fun to be called a task.

Susanne's week included walking out of a coffee shop without paying. At the supermarket she marched to the front of the queue despite the grumbles of everyone behind her. She hadn't paid any of the household bills that week, and she spilled coffee on Victor's sister-in-law. The latter, she admitted with a smile, she had always secretly wanted to do. She even managed to be out of the house for a few of Victor's telephone calls. But mostly she had liked it when he rang to ask how her day was going.

During this session Victor mentioned that something which troubled him was Susanne's jealousy. When they went to parties, she always kept an eye on him, and she wanted to go home early if she thought he was too involved or interested in some other woman. It was a paradoxical complaint, he admitted, because, if anything, he craved more physical affection from her. He enjoyed talking with other people, but he wasn't interested in getting involved with other women. He wanted to expand the physical aspect of their relationship. She admitted it was a problem area: 'You know it's something I want too. But you know it's something I never learned.'

'Are you sure it's something you want to learn? Do you feel affection for Victor? Is it something you want to show him? Well, then do it now. Express it without words.' Susanne left her chair and went to where he sat. She lifted her hand hesitantly and stroked his hair and his cheek. Then she moved her chair so she was facing him, and she took both his hands and looked in his face. Victor returned Susanne's look, with big tears in his eyes. After some moments, I conjectured:

'Victor, my guess is that you will have to work hard to stay the expert in this area. Susanne is going to learn very quickly as far as I can see it.' They both laughed softly. 'So now you have shown that you can do it. Do you think that you can find the time and opportunity for some open affection each day? Fine.'

They mentioned that they were going to a party in the week to come. I wondered if they could make a contest of the party for themselves. 'A contest?' they asked together.

'At this party you are to find out which of you can hug the most people. Men and women. The winner can ask the other person for a special favour — as unusual as you like. Each of you should keep count of your own hugs or embraces at this party. Each of you controls your own behaviour.'

They both entered my office grinning at the next session. Susanne announced that she had won the contest at the party. When I asked what her special favour of Victor was, she smiled impishly and asked if it was absolutely necessary to tell. Suddenly Victor began to cry.

'I am so pleased to see Susanne doing so well. To see her so happy again. Happier than I have ever seen her. But I'm also scared.'

'Scared?' Susanne echoed him.

'To see you growing and changing so much. I'm pleased to see you enjoying life more. But it scares me. To think that if you change, it must alter our relationship. Or that I must change in some way. And I don't know what that means for me.'

'Victor, you have stated clearly what many people who come to my office are unable to say. That it is very frightening to see your spouse grow or to do new things. But at the same time it is frightening, it is also challenging. If you have a relationship as rich as yours and Susanne's then this must be only one of many challenges you encounter. And I'm quite sure that you'll be able to meet this one.'

I asked if they were going to any parties in the coming weekend. (This was a couple who went out virtually every weekend.) They were to attend a large celebration for the fiftieth wedding anniversary of Victor's parents.

'Perfect!' I said. 'Then your task for this week is very clear. As soon as your father has made his speech for your mother [speeches are an important feature of any formal Danish celebration], you Victor are to spring to your feet. You will make a prepared speech in honour of your wife. In this speech, you are to include all the merits and all the unpredictable changes you have observed during the years you have been married to Susanne.'

Susanne was learning to value the qualities which enabled her to cope with the life she had chosen to live. She was also learning that she could make other choices, choices that were less painful or demanding, and which gave her other possibilities for her development. Victor had his task, and I warned her that her next task was probably more difficult.

She had telephoned her old friends and family when she was in the early stages of her crisis, without any positive response from them. She had also mentioned some women she met and liked at a course she had attended in the previous year. She had not had much contact with them since then, but she spoke of them warmly during one of our sessions. I told her to ring them and to invite them to her home. She was to discuss her recent difficulties, describe that she liked them and needed their support, and to get some encouragement or a positive response from them. She was shocked at the suggestion. She agreed that hers was a much more difficult task than Victor's, but she also agreed to try it.

Of course both succeeded in their tasks. Without discussing the purpose of the tasks, we spent the final session reviewing the past and planning for the future. Susanne was ready to return to her job. She recognized that any future battles were first with herself. Once she set her priorities she could manage whatever demands her professional or personal life presented. She needed to define a reasonable work pace, and to learn to delegate more responsibility to others. She had gained a new sense of the importance of her leisure time, and she had very rapidly learned new ways to enjoy herself. She learned these things more quickly than one would have thought possible, from the impression she gave at her first interview.

Intervention is the means through which the therapist influences the patient to bring about change so that his or her original complaint is resolved to satisfaction (Fisch *et al.* 1982, p. 127). In Susanne and Victor's story, the brief therapist employs structured activities or tasks.

Tasks are formulated to arrange the ways in which the patient relates to others. At the same time as they aim to influence the management of the problem, tasks can be structured so as to increase positive transactions, promote agreement between persons and elicit positive feedback, and to sanction new — perhaps previously untried — behaviour. It is possible that this can include good feelings, and even a sense of fun. The activities that the patient is directed to perform reorganize established relationships, require a breaking of rules, and extend the boundaries of what is regarded by the patient or his family as acceptable, good, or reasonable (Madanes 1981; Minuchin and Fishman 1981; Watzlawick 1976).

It is essential that the therapist gather information about the people involved in the problem, actions taken to solve the problem, and the outcome of any such efforts. The therapist needs to know what solutions have been attempted in order to learn what to avoid. The attempted solution itself is often the prolonging or aggravating element, for example where family members try to cheer up a depressed family member, or convince an alcoholic not to drink. Sometimes a complete reversal of the existing behaviour, or a new tactic other than that already attempted is required to resolve the problem. Hence, instead of getting Susanne to stop ringing Victor at work, which Victor had tried to do without success, the therapist instructed Victor to ring her.

When formulating specific tasks, the therapist seeks to identify which transactions occur most repetitively in the performance of the problem and attempts a solution. The therapist then aims to alter some aspect of the problematic transaction and attempts either to break or prevent repetition of the problematic sequence or pattern.

In Susanne's case, her disease represented advanced consequences of over-responsibility. Her symptoms and the descriptions both she and Victor provided, characterized the behaviour of the over-responsible individual: difficulties in asking for or receiving help, inability to delegate to others, assumption of too many tasks and duties, unrealistically high expectations of self and situations, low self-tolerance of imperfection.

The therapist's initial response to Susanne's problem formulation was to encourage, even prescribe, the behaviour or attitude that the patient portrayed herself resisting. In her first brief meeting with the therapist, Susanne is advised to behave as one ought to on sick leave. She is warned rather than reassured that her symptoms might mean more than discomfort for her, if she gives herself time to attend to them. Nor does she receive consolation that her problem will be relieved rapidly. The brief therapist does not enter into the patient's rejection of or impatience with her symptoms, but accepts her definition of the situation and underlines the gravity of its consequences for her. So in the case of Susanne:

'Yes, it's clear that you must not be well. You look ill. In which case you ought to take advantage of your sick leave while you can.'

or to a depressed patient:

'I understand you are depressed. Given what you have told me about your circumstances, I am surprised you're able to function as well as you do. Some people get physically sick under such stress as you're bearing now.'

or to an anxious patient:

'I can tell you are upset and worried. But your reaction is a normal one — and useful too — for these feelings will help prepare you for a situation that will probably get worse before it gets better.'

Tasks can be utilized to stimulate reflective, cogitative activities by the patient. These may be those he or she is unsuccessfully attempting to deny, or resist. They may be the sort of deliberations for which the patient has not allocated personal time and energy. Robert, as many of the patients described herein, had 'simply' not allotted himself time to take stock of the factors that were undergoing transformations in his life.

Else repeatedly apologized in her first session for occupying herself with the past. She was instructed to go home, and examine yet again all that had passed, to see if she could discover any better or different ways she would have managed things. It was after she reported the results of her self-examination, once she stopped resisting it, that she ceased discussing the past and began to consider her present circumstances and the possibilities for her future.

Tasks and structured activities can be usefully prescribed to alter social interchanges. Encounters are structured to force the patient to relate within her social network, to elicit responses other than those which contributed to the problem. Susanne was first instructed to be less perfect, and to make conscious mistakes in her life.

Because of its unexpected nature, the task refocused her energy and attention in the week she worked on it. Moreover, it required that she become more observant of factors in her social environment, and that she use her own resources in a novel, 'unproductive' fashion. At the end of treatment, she was required to demand of other persons the sort of assistance she needed in her time of acute distress.

Tasks are similarly employed to alter the transactions in which the problem is repeatedly enacted or reinforced. In formulating tasks towards this end, the therapist needs to assess what action would constitute a change from the way the situation is currently handled. A task may demand unusual or unexpected behaviour, or, conversely, foster small, seemingly irrelevant variations. The task of hugging people at the party playfully altered Susanne's pattern of jealous observation and control. It culminated in a pleasurable surprise that furthered the couple's expressed desire for more intimacy.

The brief therapist does not aim to resolve all the difficulties that seem to be present. As Robert's disappointment over his son's marriage was not pursued in discussion, nor were Susanne's feelings about her previous marriage. Treatment holds to the issues which the family present. Victor's tasks stemmed from his perception of the consequences of Susanne's condition *for him*. By ringing Susanne daily, he was able to demonstrate his concern, and at the same time control the interruption her calls caused him.

Victor's speech, using the opportunity his parents' anniversary provided, required that he disarm his worries about the couple's future. This intervention drew its inspiration from the maxim 'the best line of defence is attack', where the client is encouraged to grasp a situation or initiate a transaction previously avoided.

Tasks are structured so as to be acceptable to the persons meant to perform them. They ought to be fulfillable. It helps if they suit the behaviour and personal style of the persons involved. Because of their manifest attraction to difficult challenges, each of Susanne and Victor's tasks were presented as formidable. Each new accomplishment was accepted by the therapist with no praise, and countered with a new, more difficult task for the week to follow.

The therapist uses the outcome of tasks to establish and develop the notion that the individual or the situation is improving. This is done by building on the success of task accomplishment. It is done in several ways. The butcher's non-compliance with a task, for example, was strategically interpreted as his crafty way of leaving space for his wife to receive more attention.

The most difficult challenge for the patient was prescribed near the end of treatment. It was one Susanne had to face on her own. In her initial presentation of her circumstances, Susanne described her attempts to contact friends and family without helpful results, her recurring assumption of responsibility for the execution of professional and home tasks, and her difficulty in delegating duties or asking for assistance. A significant achievement for her would be to take initiative in requesting something for herself, from others. The purpose in directing her to invite persons she felt sympathetic to her home, and opening herself to them, was never discussed with Susanne. She fulfilled the task accepting its meaning for her as given.

This task went to the heart of the behaviour that led to her collapse. Mastery over her previous tasks — seeing that neither she nor anyone else died if she made mistakes, that she and Victor could be more expressive and open to each other and to outsiders, and that she could have fun demanding and receiving — prepared her for this undertaking. At this stage, whether these friends responded or not was not as important as Susanne's contacting them.

The strategy behind Susanne's task is to create an alternative which is more difficult than the problem presented. In a typical demonstration of this method, a patient complained that she was always being taken advantage of. Exploration of her style of managing situations showed that she tended to take care of the needs of all those around her, and that she took rather poor care of her own concerns.

'Well, I know that it's possible for you to learn to stop letting people take advantage of you,' her therapist said, 'but the lesson is a terribly difficult one, and I don't really know if you're up to it.'

'But . . .'

'And it's the sort of thing I don't even want to describe unless you'd be willing to do it. For it's not the sort of thing one *tries* to do. The instructions must be followed exactly if it is to be effective.'

'You think it can help me?'

'I know it can help, but I'm not . . .'

'Then I want to do it!'

'Well, OK, but . . . you're sure?'

'Just tell me and I'll do it!'

The client was instructed to do her grocery shopping at the time she knew the store would be most crowded. She was told to join the longest line with her purchases. When she reached the head of the line, she should give her place to the person behind her and return to the end of the line. She should repeat this sequence as many times as possible, and she was to find at least five occasions to go shopping and to carry out the task before reporting back in a week's time.

Finally, while apt instructions can be seen to be effective, it is wise for the therapist to keep in mind that if she or he cannot find a task, or cannot think of any useful activity to prescribe, then none should be given: 'You've probably heard that I usually give people 'homework' but I don't think we need to do that after all we've covered today.' Or, 'You are going through so much just now, I think we can stop this session now. I won't give you any tasks this time.'

The lady in the food store illustrates one method of delivering instructions, often called 'the devil's pact' strategy, whereby the therapist elicits the patient's agreement to a plan before he knows what it is (Watzlawick *et al.* 1974; Weeks and L'Abate 1982). Authors such as Watzlawick and L'Abate present a number of methods and suggestions as to how to engage the patient in activities beyond the session. What emerges from the examples in the literature is that each therapist employs her own personality and style in interpreting the model and involving the patient in activity which interrupts the pattern or sequence of behaviour previously resulting in a problem. Susanne and Victor certainly altered the patterns that prolonged their problem, and discovered new alternatives in themselves and in their social environment.

Lena's Independence

Lena rang saying an acquaintance told her I could help her with her divorce. She wanted to come with her husband because she had decided she wanted to divorce him.

The couple were in their early thirties. Lena was 31. A psychiatric nurse, she was more plump than becoming. Her brown hair was boyishly cut and she peered over the top of her glasses with light brown eyes. As she described her need to be independent, she leaned towards me with her arms bent and her fists on her thighs. Daniel was 30. He worked as a teacher in an institution for mentally handicapped adults. He was thin, and had light blonde hair, and a blonde beard. He thought they had a good marriage together.

Lena said she had used Daniel as a father figure in the time they were together. She repeated that she now needed to be independent. She repeated that she was quite sure she wanted a divorce. But she was also frightened that she might easily be influenced to change her mind.

Daniel was quiet. As Lena spoke, he smiled in an indulgent way. When it was his turn to speak, he told of the different ideas Lena had had over their years together. He could only imagine that this was a new one. Wanting a divorce was surely a natural consequence of her newly conceived notion of becoming more independent.

It was difficult getting a realistic discussion started in this first session.

Lena maintained that the past years had been an experimental attempt to revive something which was long dead. They had moved to Jutland and built a new house. They had a baby, a little girl now just a year old. Both of them worked part time in order to be able to be together with the little girl as much as possible. But nothing improved a marriage which began deteriorating years ago.

Lena did not have any fixed plans for her future. She knew that a nuclear family structure could not give her what she craved of life. She imagined that she would live alone with the little girl for a while and eventually end up in a collective where other single adults lived with their children.

Daniel forced a laugh as he told about the past year. Lena had refined her feminism and self-reliance to the extent that she insisted on chopping all their firewood last winter. And now — he paused. And now she acted as if it were natural that she would get custody of Pauline, the little girl they both wanted so much, and planned for, and shared the care of. Even when Lena was home on maternity leave, Daniel came home early from work each day to help with her.

'Daniel, I can't hear in what you're saying, whether you've taken Lena's decision seriously or not. I think it's important for all that this point is as clear as it can be before we starting discussing the question of Pauline's custody.'

Daniel slowly repeated that he could not get beyond seeing this as another of Lena's usual 'whims'. He believed if they worked on a few of their difficulties in living together, everything would be alright — as it always had been before. When asked for an example of their difficulties, Daniel said it was a problem for him that he could no longer help Lena with anything. She became terribly angry and insulted the last time he washed her car!

'He's right!' Lena added. She didn't want his help. She wanted to manage her life herself, in her own way.

Was there anything they did together now, I asked. They slept in the same bed, apparently, and had sex together, infrequently. Sometimes they saw friends together. But Lena wanted to have her own 'separate' set of friends, so they tended to argue about keeping friends and family contacts.

By the end of the session, it was clear that Daniel, in presenting marital issues he believed might be improved, did not see divorce as the outcome of Lena's declaration. It was also clear that the manner in which Lena presented her plan made it hard to assess whether she was serious in her stated intentions or not.

They were given the task to go home and, for the week to follow, to divide their home between them: to eat, sleep and function separately. They already took turns in carrying and fetching Pauline from day care, and in feeding and bathing her. From today, they were also to take turns in having the care of her through the night.

At the following session, Daniel reported that he had slept very little during that week. He lay awake uncomfortably each night, thinking about how things had developed. He missed sleeping in the same bed with Lena. He also missed their discussions and their disagreements. Even the time he spent with Pauline felt sad and empty — and that had been the best part of the week for him.

Lena admitted she enjoyed her time alone, free to do as she liked, when she decided, and in her own way. She also admitted feeling sorry for Daniel. She expressed her hopes that he too might be able to learn that life could be much richer if one lived independently.

Daniel again repeated his belief that a marriage that lasted as long and worked as well as theirs could not simply end without reason. As a family therapist, I must be able to help them so they could continue as man and wife, father and mother. I told them both that from my experience with other couples, I believed that both partners had to want to continue if there could be any chance of positive development. I told them I would work with either or both of them, whichever route they decided on, but that they needed to be straight and open with each other at this point. I stopped talking and looked at Lena.

Lena looked back at me, then over to Daniel: 'I wish you could start appreciating the challenge of being alone.'

I stopped her, and said that what I wanted was a clear message. Daniel was asking whether she had made her decision to divorce him, or if anything could yet be done to alter their marriage so that it might continue. After a few more attempts to answer abstractly or indirectly — at which point I always intervened and repeated the basic question, Lena said 'No,' that she had thought too much and gone too far to change her decision.

Daniel turned white and asked politely if he might leave now. I took him to another room where he could be alone. I told him that if he wanted or needed to cry, he could do so there without disturbing anyone, or having anyone disturb him. Before leaving, I promised I would return soon.

I told Lena I knew how difficult it was to deliver such a painful message clearly. She knew now that she would have to meet the consequences which would follow. She should consider these in the week to come and return to discuss them.

Daniel was by now crying quietly in the room where I left him. 'She couldn't mean it's the end,' he said when I entered the room. 'She can't just sweep away our years and all we've created together — like dirt.' He continued on about the house. He had done all the carpentry work in the house on his own. They had carefully planned and worked the garden. It was just beginning to look as they dreamed it would. Lena would not settle for a home that looked like everyone else's. She had her own ideas of how it should be right from the start. How could she want to leave that now?

Daniel's deepest fears and despair centred around his daughter, his little Pauline whom he loved and longed for more than anything else. In shock after Lena's announcement, he repeated his concerns in various sequences and forms through the next half hour. When he decided he was ready to go home, we arranged to meet again in three days to review his overall situation, and to discuss further any issues he wanted to pursue.

Until our next meeting, I told him very simply, he should allow himself to be as unhappy and as angry as he felt. Nor should he resist telling Lena how unhappy he was.

'Both of you are responsible for what happens from now on — so it will be important that you become as familiar as possible with each other's reactions and thoughts.' As I saw him to the door I added, 'And I want you to continue to have good contact with Pauline. To play with her and cuddle her. Enjoy her as much as you can. She'll need that, and she'll repay you for your attentions.'

Daniel returned still unhappy, and by now very angry at Lena for ruining his life. 'Maybe if she'd found another man, it might be easier,' he said early in the session. Later on, he added, 'Well, at least she's not fallen in love with anyone else. That's some small relief.'

Most clearly and passionately he expressed the meaning Pauline provided for his life. He wanted full custody of her and reckoned that since Lena was abandoning their home, his getting custody had to be the only sensible outcome. At the end of this session he was instructed to consider the advantages for Pauline should he have full custody, then he should return with Lena at the time of her next appointment.

Daniel and Lena modified the instructions following their first session. They still shared their house, if on somewhat separate terms. Before returning for this conjoint meeting, they seriously discussed the terms of care for Pauline. They wanted shared custody.

I had to inform them that Denmark has no legal provision for joint or shared custody. One parent alone can hold legal custody in cases of divorce. At this bit of news both shot upright in their chairs, mouths in taut lines across their faces, glowering at each other and at me. Neither had done any research on this or any other legal aspect of their circumstances.[1] My information blocked the solution they took so long to come to, and they could see no alternatives in that moment.

I asked if they had considered what would be best for Pauline. Daniel was, of course, prepared for the question. In his care, Pauline need not be removed from her familiar surroundings. He had worked out the economics of the situation and it was clear that with his position and salary, he could maintain the family household on his own. He believed it unlikely that he would remarry. He intended to devote himself to raising his child in the best way possible. On the other hand, he felt Lena would surely find another man, or move Pauline around before settling anywhere.

Lena conceptualized the solution in another way. Were she to have custody of Pauline, she envisaged Pauline living one week with her, the next with Daniel. They would truly share the raising of their daughter. Lena knew virtually nothing about the family finances, but she imagined that with what she would get from a settlement on their house, she could manage a flat in town. She guessed that neither of them could afford the house without taking on more work, and that was unrealistic for it meant cutting down the time for child care, which was what they were arguing about after all.

'The two solutions are rather unlike,' I stated simply. 'Do you think it's possible to try out some of these ideas now, before you undertake legal action? So you have some experience as well as ideas to base your settlements on?'

They looked at each other silently for a few moments, then Lena offered to move in with a friend for the present. A friend from work, recently divorced, had spoken of being lonely in her house, so Lena believed she would be pleased to have company. And Lena was not particularly attached to the house they now shared anyway. Daniel proffered that he take Pauline the first week, then they agreed on details of her care for the next four weeks.

Daniel wondered then about the effects of the upheaval on Pauline.

Lena replied that she was really too small to react to their separation. I informed them that children younger than Pauline react with physical symptoms when their parents had trouble living together. Even if it was a difficult time for them as adults just now ('But it's not for me!' Lena interjected), as individual parents they should give her a calm, pleasant time with them, and all the affection she needed, and take note if Pauline showed any stress reactions — trouble sleeping, unusual eating behaviour, or if she seemed worried or unusually active. Their decisions affected her world, and it was their responsibility that she still have the love and care she needed to thrive.

Three weeks later Daniel rang to request a final meeting. He said he had reached a decision, but he wanted to deliver it to Lena in my company. He thought he might need some support, and really had no one else to turn to.

With all three of us together, Daniel stated that he could not continue. The weeks that he had Pauline with him in the house, he felt bad. In the week when Lena had Pauline, he spent each day waiting for her return. Being allowed to visit her at Lena's only made an empty week worse. He was not happy with her, and miserable waiting in the time he was without her.

Lena replied that she was quite satisfied with their agreement. She missed Pauline a bit during Daniel's weeks, but she also appreciated the time without her.

'Then what do you think about Daniel's comments? Could you imagine having her for shorter periods?'

Lena did not hesitate in replying that any arrangement should be as equal as they had always tried to make it. To which Daniel answered that either he would have full custody or else he wanted to limit his time with Pauline to brief visits once or twice a month. He could not handle the current arrangement. Of that he was sure.

'So, we appear to be where we started. But now you both have some experience of sharing the care of Pauline. One of you does not feel able to cope with the conditions that creates. Daniel, you want either full custody or to restrict your visits to once or twice a month. Lena, you say you want to divide each month equally. It's difficult to see how to make a decision that will satisfy you both.

'I want you to know that you may take this issue to court. This process takes a very long time. It will make demands on your time, your nerves, and your economy, and won't necessarily give more security than you can create between yourselves. From my experience, it is rare for a child not to be influenced by the stresses which accompany this legal process. It is not my intention to frighten you, but rather to give you some idea of what legal action involves. Most people enter it having no notion.

'It's my view that parents have responsibility on many levels and in a variety of areas. Taking care of oneself, and one's development as an adult certainly are parts of behaving responsibly. You have both discovered degrees of this, from what I know of you.

'It sounds from what you say, Daniel — and please correct me if I'm wrong — that just now you cannot see that it's feasible or realistic for you to continue with Pauline on the terms you have tried. You find it painful when she is with you, since you know that time will soon end and the time you wait for her to come is even worse.' I stopped talking and looked at him.

Lena sat quietly and looked at Daniel. The room was very still, and I think it felt warm to us all. Daniel looked all around the room — at the floor, and the ceiling, at the furniture and the walls. Then he exhaled deeply and looked at me:

'But I never wanted *any* of this. I was happy as it was.' Then he looked away again.

'I've seen how terribly hard this time has been for you,' I said. 'I believe you worked your best to make the kind of family life you wanted, and I know what a shock it is to hear that it hasn't worked out as you hoped and trusted it would. It's always a shock. Especially when you are presented with a plan you never wanted to begin with.

'And now we sit here trying to come up with a plan for the future — to try to find ways you can continue with as little suffering as possible — for you or for Pauline.'

This time Daniel didn't ask for permission, he just left the room. Lena and I looked at each other. 'I think I'd better go too,' she said.

'I think that's right,' I replied.

Daniel rang early the next morning to say he had decided to drop his idea about having custody of Pauline. It was a decision he did not want to discuss further or have to defend. He would contact Lena to inform her that she could have custody, that they could arrange to split all their belongings 50–50, and that he would decide which days he would visit Pauline.

'Since we started sharing Pauline I've considered the aspects of this thing. Of course I'm not happy with it — not happy in any way — but I think that this decision gives me another perspective on my future. I don't want to remain in that house we built together — on lies I now see — and I can't imagine living with the torment that week-with/week-without Pauline arrangement means for me. I don't want to live the rest of my life on Lena's terms. I don't know what I'll feel in 6 or 12 months' time, but I'll stand by what I say now, and hope I can maintain a good relationship with Pauline.' And he was gone from the line as quickly as he had been there.

Lena rang a few hours later. She sounded as if in shock, and she said that Daniel's news made her very anxious. She feared he might do something rash — there was a history of mental illness in his family.

'You have decided to end your contact with this man. Taking care of him, if you are serious about leaving him, will confuse him. If I understand him he has made some decisions he intends to stand by. Your main job now is to concentrate on the practicalities and the new responsibilities you have for your child. That will be job enough.'

Divorce counselling has been the largest single category for which patients at Laegernes Hus present themselves in explicit need of assistance. They present either during the process of parting, or for help in the aftermath.

Clinical experience (a) with the sorts of problems with which patients came forward: child custody and visiting rights, physical symptomatology, depression and bereavement reactions (such as trouble in sleeping, non-specific head or body aches), or physical or behavioural problems with children and (b) with the characteristic problems which accompany divorce work: intense arguing in session, attempted manipulation to make the therapist look after the welfare of one ex-partner, difficulties in eliciting communication for negotiating settlements, persistent efforts to injure or take revenge on an ex-spouse to the detriment of the children's welfare, and the like, influenced an adaptation of problem-focused brief therapy for these cases.

Affective or insight-orientated models were employed in divorce cases early on in the psychosocial integration at Laegernes Hus. Differential outcomes suggested that a brief approach which took into account the reaction modes which attend divorce or separation was the most fruitful for the demands of the patients.

Brief intervention in divorce work concentrates on the specific issue for which assistance is sought. Avoidance of prolonged professional involvement allows the splitting partners to proceed with the 'work' of divorce. This 'work' of divorce consists of meeting the personal reactions and the social circumstances into which divorce forces the individual, and resolving these in ways that are constructive for the individual, for his future, and for other persons who may be involved.

Krantzler's separation shock (1975), a phenomenon described by members of divorce groups and schematized by Krantzler, provides a useful conceptual model of the personal, affective phases experienced by individuals undergoing the lengthy separation process. The phases are listed in sequential order:

- initial denial that the relationship has ended
- retreat into fantasy life where the marriage lives on
- powerful feelings of anger and hostility at having been abandoned (these often experienced by the divorcer as well as the divorced)
- pervasive feelings of guilt — internalized or projected — over actions not taken, or taken during the relationship (if only I had/ hadn't . . .)
- withdrawal from parts of the past (persons, memories, activities) too painful to cope with in the present
- gradual testing and retesting of reality (in social behaviour, new modes of dress, interests, and activities)
- letting go from influences of past relationship, development of new relationships, personal strengths and interests

(p. 92)

The scheme serves as a reference for therapist and divorcee alike. It can assist the therapist identify the not uncommonly irrational behaviour of the individual in divorce as a predictable reaction mode, and not a symptom to be assuaged. As input to the divorced/divorcing client, it helps set puzzling responses into perspective, and underscores their transitory nature. This last feature should not be underrated, as patients report being frightened by unexpected or uncharacteristic behaviour in themselves which divorce or another crisis sets into action (cf. Lindemann 1944).

Another serviceable model which conceptualizes stages of the divorce process is that presented by Bohannan, an anthropologist who has written of American divorce (*The Six Stations of Divorce* 1971).

The emotional divorce — Bohannan says this begins with a realization that a couple do not have a constructive future together. An inability to tolerate change in a partner, or to perceive benefits from individual growth is credited as the key factor which conduces termination of a marriage. The gratification that accompanied the thrill of being selected for engagement and marriage is supplanted by the anger and hurt of deselection or rejection of divorce.

The legal divorce — formal action which voids the marriage contract and creates remarriageability. This station frequently generates bewilderment. The parties have no control over proceedings and are swept along by protocol and the legal events themselves.

One of the reasons that the divorce institution is so hard on people is that the legal processes do not provide an orderly and socially approved discharge of emotions that are elicited during the emotional divorce and during the early part of preparations for the legal processes. (p. 48)

The economic divorce — division of money and material goods previously shared in practice or name by the adults concerned. Rarely

82

an easy reapportionment, economic issues are not uncommonly complicated by advice from lawyers or friends. The economic divorce is a station at which unfinished emotional battles can be covertly pursued through protracted and detailed disputation over objects and cash.

Co-parental divorce — is concerned with questions of the physical custody of children: where they will live; responsibility for raising the children, which includes the degree to which the activities of the children are limited as well as the opportunities that are created for them during their childhood and youth; and visitation rights. In the parental divorce, there is also the issue of how much to involve children in the event itself: how much ought they be told about the cause of divorce; how to include their wishes in custodial plans. Bohannan identifies this station as the most worrisome and guilt-provoking for the divorcing parent.

The community divorce — marks the shift in status which the individual holds in his social circles. Just as the social network alters at marriage — to include new friends and family — it restructures at the announcement of divorce. The newly divorced may be left unsure about previously secure sources of support, affection and companionship (cf. also Krantzler 1975; Weiss 1975).

The psychic divorce — Bohannan regards this as the final station, a lonesome and often fearsome process by which the individual becomes 'himself or herself again . . . an autonomous social individual' (p. 36). In separating the self from the influence of the ex-spouse, the divorced individual employs and therefore develops new facets of character, new strengths, and new relationships in his personal community. Examination of the reasons for getting married in the first place, and the reasons for getting divorced can provide the individual with insights to his own self-regard and approach to life. These in turn enhance the development of the personal autonomy which Bohannan conceives as the constructive resolution of the psychic divorce.

What schemes such as these illuminate, is that the impact of separation or divorce is neither singular nor static. It is characterized by phases which are distinct from one another, yet are dynamic, frequently repetitive, and which may vary in terms of time span and affective intensity. The ways in which the individual passes through these phases, or confronts the challenge or troubles which arise with them, is believed to determine the eventual outcome of the separation process. This means that the degree to which the individual accommodates to his altered status is the key to his eventual well-being — whether he achieves individual 'autonomy' or establishes new personal networks, or whether he manifests physical symptoms or becomes pathologically fixated at one of the stages.

The distinct stages of the reaction–adaptation process outlined above most often occur at varied paces in the individuals involved. This uneven pacing can be seen in all the divorce cases in this collection. From the beginning of the first session, the therapist took seriously the problem that one partner, Lena, talked about divorce, and the other, Daniel, denied comprehension of Lena's statements.

The preliminary aim here, as in most divorce work at Laegernes Hus, was to help the couple find the grounds on which they could discuss and co-operate (or at least negotiate) over issues such as responsible custody of their child. It is not an aim of this work that partners remain on friendly terms, but rather that negotiations can lead to agreements that are reasonable, realistic and wherein all concerned can retain his and her integrity.

Initially, the therapist strives to obtain a picture of how the couple are living at present. This includes details of how they currently organize their daily lives, whether they function as if they have a future together, existing patterns of communication, and whether there is a lover or other persons involved. It is also important to find out whether one or either have begun preparing for the separation. This information helps the therapist assist in assessing what grounds exist, and what problems the couple have in communicating. It must be clear whether the couple are seeking reconciliation or separation. Both their behaviour and their contrasting descriptions of the circumstances highlighted the difficulties between Lena and Daniel. Lena, for example, was quite capable of communicating directly to the therapist what she wanted, but unable or unwilling to take the consequences of such interaction with Daniel.[2]

A primary object of the work at Laegernes Hus was to prepare both parties to negotiate the emotional and practical intricacies of separation. The individual was encouraged to recognize personal responses, to trust that these responses have significance as reactions to a critical life event, and to exercise sensitivity and judgement in devising a future, rather than leaving fundamental issues (such as the question of who will have care of the children) to others.

Interventions are designed to raise or uphold the self-esteem of the individual in a seriously debilitating situation. Overt enthusiasm or encouragement is not held to be effective or useful. Tasks are focused on issues which are immediately important to the individual and on the aspects of the issue which he can influence. Daniel could not control the outcome of any struggle over custody, but he could assess and determine what he believed would be best for Pauline, and for himself.

The fact that neither Lena nor Daniel had checked on the legislation was evidence that neither had sufficiently thought through their intentions. Their task of trying out different forms of household division and management aimed to prepare the parties for decisions that needed to be made in the course of their divorce. Few couples reverse their decision to separate, but a week of eating and sleeping alone, or going to a pub or a film as single, influences many to alter original notions about the challenges and benefits of being on their own. This testing of possible consequences has been seen to enable individuals to take more studied decisions about the future, rather than continuing assumptions and patterns of behaviour which may have led them into divorce. Still, the therapist must always be prepared that recently divorced people may act in unexpected ways.

Daniel's withdrawal from the joint custody proposal represents a version of the pattern of fathers who leave their offspring in the mother's care. This tendency was found amongst fathers in a recent study of joint-custody families in New York (Rothberg 1983):

> Thirty percent of the [sample] population felt that it was a hindrance . . . . It is interesting to note that no women felt that joint custody was a hindrance to forming new relationships . . . . It was the men who felt it was a hindrance. These feelings are in keeping with the traditional sex-role expectations of women maintaining the children after divorce and of men expecting to be free . . . (p. 45)

Responsibility and rational planning are particularly stressed with regard to the details of child care. While this story does not include a child old enough to demonstrate its tolerance of its parents' divorce, the story shows how parents minimize the effects of their actions on their children. Emphasis on the trauma of divorce for adults can be seen to have led to inconsideration of the needs of children caught in litigation, or negligence on the part of emotionally spent parents. Too many children are caught in the promiscuous morass between parents who cannot get on, yet who cannot 'leave' each other (Francke 1983). Even where family conditions may improve following a divorce, children inevitably suffer. The therapist upholds the responsibility of the parents not to deny or sugar-coat the consequences of divorce, but to fulfil their parental role in supporting each child who goes through his own separation shock.

Parents must discover in themselves how best to fulfil their parental obligations. The therapist must beware of the pitfalls of adopting current fashions of appropriate parental or divorce etiquette – that, for example, the best divorced parents are 'friends' or that joint custody is the most responsible option. Daniel's decision to relinquish his claim for Pauline marked the start of his disengagement from Lena. His subsequent relationship with Pauline would develop distinctly and on its own. The therapist here did not reprimand or judge, but rather stressed that he meet the responsibilities he could, and that he keep the door open for fuller future contact.

Divorce counselling has a reputation of being more arduous than other forms of couples work. Behaviour such as intense arguing, two adults manifesting conflicting shock reactions at different paces (detachment v. sorrow, guilt v. denial, and so on), and the relative instability and irrationality which characterize all the reaction modes means that it is hard work for all involved. Sticking closely to the problem-formulation techniques of brief therapy has proved useful to help the therapist avoid either urging a couple to a premature decision or inhibiting the articulation of a decision that has already been made. It also helps the therapist avoid entering explosive emotional territory which has no relevance for the issue at hand. Divorce counselling at Laegernes Hus has been based on experience rather than science, and a trust that the pain of early divorce reactions is followed by reparation and reorientation which opens on to new opportunities (what Krantzler calls the 'promise in the pain', p. 36). These help the therapist sustain a hopeful — and realistic — tone through interventions made.

Henrietta's Choice

'The doctor said last night that you would help Henrietta. That you could find out what was the matter with her. Help her understand she should be happy to have a good job and get back to it. So we could stop being so worried.'

The speaker was tall, with a ruddy face and curly reddish hair. He squared himself uneasily on his chair, where he kept crossing one leg over the other. He looked to be a little over 40, and he looked very worried. His eyes darted from his wife to the teenager with them, to me and back to his wife again.

Before I could respond, his wife added, 'Yes! And if it were up to me, Henrietta would have been admitted to hospital last night. Then the right people would have responsibility for someone who behaves that way, and we'd all feel more secure. I'm beside myself with anxiety! First thing this morning I had to ring for nerve tablets for myself, and I've had to ask for sick leave. There was no question of going to work and trying to concentrate there — you must be able to understand that.'

The slim, angular woman in the chair opposite me trembled as she contributed her piece. Her dark eyes mirrored her worry in a face that betrayed the life she had lived. Tora was 37 — an age her body responded to well enough, but her face was that of a person 10 years older. Her brow was wrinkled and deep lines cut at the side of her mouth and along the sides of her nose. The hands which she constantly ran through her dark, waved hair, were long and elegantly formed, but testified to years of hard work.

Henrietta occupied the third chair. She closely resembled her mother, but for a fullness that bordered on corpulence. Nearly 18 years of age, her hair had the same colour and texture as her mother's, her hands the same length, yet broader. She was very pale, as was her mother, and she sat just now extraordinarily still.

I told them I could not guarantee that I could find out what the matter was with Henrietta, but that I could probably assist Stephen and Tora to help her. That made Henrietta look up at me.

'Was there something you wanted to say, Henrietta?'

'They won't get me out there again.'

Tora took this declaration as her cue: 'Can you understand anybody even thinking of trying to . . . and then to *do* what she did! Just because they think they don't want to continue in a good position. And today when it is so difficult to get any job. And then *such* a job! I can't understand it. And with so many people hanging around with their hands in their pockets. Wanting to get some work, but not able to — I can't believe that this is the main reason. There must be something else!'

And then Stephen added, as if he were thinking out loud, 'I can't believe that suddenly it's become so bad to work there. We all see each other every day, and Henrietta never mentioned she didn't like it there.'

Throughout these comments Henrietta resumed her earlier position, sitting with her hands in her lap, looking down at her legs. She raised her head once again and said, 'I have tried so many times to tell you that I didn't like the work. But you never heard me. You never listen.'

Tora moved forward as if to speak, but a glance from her husband stopped her. And after a moment, he added, 'Perhaps we didn't listen. Perhaps we might have done things in another way.' He looked at me.

I asked Henrietta to leave the room, saying that I would recall her when I had spoken alone with her parents. I asked them to describe what had taken place the night before.

Tora began by explaining that she worked second shift at a local textile factory, 4 to 11 p.m. each evening but Friday. It was an arrangement she preferred because it meant she could be at home during the day with Belinda, her younger daughter. She made it her habit, on returning home late each night, to look in on both daughters, to see that they were safe in bed, to say goodnight to Henrietta if she were still awake.

Last night Tora had as usual looked in on Henrietta, but she sensed that something was amiss. The room was abnormally quiet, and she wasn't able to stir Henrietta. It was impossible to awaken her. Tora rushed to the bathroom and found what she most feared. The bottle of sleeping-pills she kept on the top shelf was empty. She rang the doctor on duty immediately and woke her husband.

The doctor questioned Tora about the number of sleeping-pills left in the bottle. How many had Henrietta swallowed? He assured them that there was no danger from the pills available. She would wake up with a bad hangover, but she ought to sleep off the overdose and wake on her own.

Tora and Stephen pressed the GP to take her to hospital that night. She had to be very sick to behave in this way. But the doctor resisted their arguments, saying that it was an important opportunity to learn what was troubling Henrietta. If they admitted her to hospital they might lose the opportunity to find out what was behind it. He remained to talk with the couple for some time. He returned early this morning on his way to the clinic, to look in on Henrietta and to recommend the three of them to come in to see me that same day.[3]

The couple trusted their doctor, and so they sat before me — even if Tora was frightened and wanted immediately to place Henrietta somewhere where they knew how to handle people who tried such things. She concluded her description with an expression of her fear that perhaps Henrietta had inherited her delicate nerves. Tora herself had received treatment in psychiatric wards more than once when she was younger.

Stephen supplemented Tora's story with his recollection of a time about seven years earlier when Henrietta had a bout of stomach-aches at school. The teacher said Henrietta had fainted, and she was sent home. No physical reasons were ever found, and the pains stopped spontaneously. He wondered if these were related to what took place last night. 'Perhaps she also wanted to tell us something at that time,' he said. After a considerable pause he added, 'But if there is anything we can change, I'm willing to do it. If there is somewhere we've gone wrong, I am willing to do anything to help her now.'

Tora suggested that it might have to do with the death of Henrietta's grandfather. They had always been very close.

'But,' Stephen said, 'I'm sure I took care of that. I'm sure she doesn't think of that any longer.' And he recounted how, the day before her grandfather suddenly died, Henrietta visited him and had done some errands for him. She used some of his change from the errands to buy sweets for herself. The very next day, he died. She wept and wept, and finally whispered to Stephen what she had done.

'Now, do you remember how much of Grandpa's money you used?' Stephen had asked her. 'Then you write Grandpa a little note, explaining what happened and how you feel now, and we'll take that same amount of money, and put them both in an envelope and place it in Grandpa's coffin. Then he'll know you didn't mean to keep the money.'

'Ah, that was a fine solution. And how old was Henrietta when that happened?'

'She must have been about 10 or 11,' Stephen replied, looking over towards Tora for confirmation.

'Well, you see,' Tora continued, 'what I mean that the work can't be the only reason. There must be something else she doesn't want to tell us.

'The girl has no real friends. She spends all her free time alone in her room drawing or with those horrible romance magazines.'

Stephen corroborated the fact that Henrietta had always seemed to have difficulties in finding friends. He felt sure that she was healthy, but perhaps she needed another job, or something — another way to occupy herself. But he would be the first to vouch that she was willing and able to work. She did so every year at the farm, and there was nothing wrong with her work there.

I told them I could see how much they worried about their daughter's welfare. What she probably most needed now was to see their interest in her. I wanted them all to return in three days. Until then they were not to discuss anything at all with Henrietta about the job. They could ask her to help around the house, and they could certainly tell her if they worried about the way she behaved.

To Stephen I added that it would be especially fine if he could show Henrietta a little extra attention: it was important for girls of her age to get some kind of attention from their fathers.

'Tora, you've said how much this has upset you. To worry about Henrietta is a perfectly normal and appropriate way to react. And you might not get over that reaction before we meet next time. All the same, I think you ought to get back to work as soon as possible. I understand you're off this evening — that makes sense — but I don't think your staying at home will help anything, and one sick family member seems quite enough.' I commended her for discovering Henrietta's state and for dealing so capably with it. Her pattern of looking in on her children said much about how she fulfilled her role as mother — even if she combined that role with a taxing job.

The first thing Henrietta told me when we were alone was how much she hated her job. She always loved flowers and ever since she was a little girl she found it exciting to put flowers together in different forms and arrangements. They always told her she would be a gardener or a florist, and it never occurred to her that she could be anything else. So after a basic year at a professional training school, it seemed enormously good luck to find a position with a florist. This shop was one of the largest in the area. They handled lots of hotel work, and exhibitions and funerals.

But she was quite unprepared for what the job demanded. Working in a florist shop — this one at least — was nothing at all like being in her garden or at her grandparents' farm, or even on her training course, where she could take as much time as she needed to work her flowers into bouquets and wreaths. Down there she had to use the flowers they ordered her to use, put them together as they directed her to, and at a dreadful pace.

'Either there was no work and everybody sat around and gossiped and smoked, or they all ran around like chickens with their heads cut off! Most of the time there was more than one deadline, more than one order to meet.' There were few chances to think about what she was doing, or even to take a few moments for herself. She felt pressed all the time. Since the others didn't look pressed, she thought, there must be something different or wrong with her. She began getting anxious about not being quick enough, no matter how fast she tried to work. Then she started being afraid to go to work, hating getting up and having to go each morning, hating each moment there.

She tried describing this to her parents — some of it in any case — but they always replied that she would get used to it. The first job was always the hardest. You couldn't quit after just three months. She had to give herself and the others a longer time. And so she stopped trying to talk about it with them. But knowing that she could not give it more time, she decided to end it all.

'It's clear that this work takes up most of your energy — with the worry and all. What else is important in your life as it is?'

Henrietta described how fond she was of her little sister. Belinda was just over a year old. Henrietta didn't know her so well since she was born at the time she was away on her floral design course, but she was someone who meant a lot to her. Did she have creative interests other than flowers? She replied that she drew quite a lot, and sometimes she read. When Henrietta returned in three days with her parents, I wanted her to bring a drawing of Belinda. 'And I know it's difficult, but for now you should stop thinking about that job. You have a lot more serious things to worry about now, and there'll be plenty of time later on to decide whether or not you'll go back.'

'But what if they bring up the work?'

'Yes. What if they talk about the work? What would happen if you said you don't want to discuss it? What would happen then?'

'My mother would get sad, and my father will get angry. And when Stephen gets angry, I get scared.'

'Just what happens when Stephen gets angry?'

'Well, he shouts very loudly. And usually I get so scared that I start to tremble, and then I try to get to my room as quickly and quietly as possible.'

'How do the others react when your father raises his voice?' She couldn't answer that. 'Then I want you to tell me next time we meet: how does your mother react, and how does Belinda react?' She promised to try to find the answers.

I started the next session by asking Henrietta to wait outside, and meeting her parents first. Tora complained about having Henrietta at home all day, not doing anything worthwhile around the house, sitting in her room, reading her magazines. Stephen described how pleased he was to come home and find Henrietta taking care of Belinda. He was impressed with how much Belinda seemed to like her big sister. He had to agree with Tora that she didn't do much on her own, but she did what he asked her to do. He couldn't get himself to worry about her becoming lazy. She had been used to helping at the farm since she was small, and she had done it each year except that year she was at school. She seemed to know where help was needed, and that's where she would be. Stephen's father owned a large dairy farm. Each spring and autumn he needed help in the fields and in the barn. Ever since they moved to Billund, Henrietta had shown interest in how the farm functioned and how she could take part in it. She learned to drive the tractor at a very early age, for example.

'Does she know you consider her a good hand?' I asked.

'I . . . think so,' he said, but he didn't look certain.

I confirmed with both parents that they had not discussed the future or her job with Henrietta, and advised them to continue to avoid those topics. They should continue that, even if it might not make sense to them to do so. After three days, Tora was still at home on sick leave. I recommended that she take up work again before too long. Furthermore, if she was irritated with Henrietta's contribution to the housework, she should demand more of her. I encouraged Stephen to mention to Henrietta what he thought of the way she worked.

Henrietta had fulfilled her task. She noted that her mother reacted in the same way she did to Stephen's anger. She became silent, and looked scared, while little Belinda seemed not to hear anything unusual. 'I think I must be most like my mother,' she concluded.

She had sketched Belinda as a 13 to 14-year-old because, she said, it was impossible to draw her now as her expressions changed all the time. The drawing showed a happy, pretty young girl with a tennis racquet in her hand. I asked her to tell me about the drawing.

'That's how I imagine her at 14. On her way to tennis, afterwards, perhaps, to a dance. But she'll do lots of sports and she'll have boyfriends and girl-friends, and she'll be happy and popular.'

'Is that how you wanted to be?'

She thought a little. 'I guess it is . . . I'm no good at any sport and I have no friends at all.' The closest thing she had to friends were some of the boys and girls who worked as hands at the farm. Tora didn't think they were suitable friends for her. Their interests were not the right ones. 'But I enjoy being together with them when I am out there.'

There was really nothing more she liked about life. She hated her work and had no particular pleasure in her leisure time. Aside from the floral design course, her only happy hours were when she helped on the farm and there had been very little of that over the past year and a half.

'But the girl in your drawing enjoys life,' I said. 'And it sounds to me as if little Belinda enjoys it now.' Henrietta replied that when a person is so small they get attention from all the grown-ups, and hardly ever get blamed for anything that goes wrong.

I told her about a little girl I once knew. She was in a very difficult situation. Her father had taken up a job in a very isolated part of the country. When the family moved, she missed her dog, and her friends, and everything that was familiar to her. In this time she discovered the importance of reviewing what happened to her during each day. She liked to do this just before she went to sleep, 'Then I am quite alone and can think,' she had told me. She only counted what she called the 'good things'. Since she was too young to write, she listed these by putting beads on a string. She used beads of different colours and sizes, to represent different qualities of her experiences. She did not have the same amount each day, but she determined to come up with at least three 'good things'. She made a string each week. Sometimes it would be short, other weeks very long and beautiful.

'Even if you are pretty young, you've had many bad experiences you could show on a string. But from what I understand you also like flowers, and gardening, and farming. These are part of your life So, like the little girl in my story, you can also recognize some of the pleasures of life. I want you to start to look for some of these 'good things'. How do you think you could illustrate them? Maybe with flowe . . .'

Her eyes lit up. 'No! I could do it with drawings!'

I looked seriously at her. 'I don't think it's an easy assignment. You'll have to take time each evening to do it. But perhaps you can see how important it is for you just now. And remember, there must be at least three things every day.'

At our next meeting I called in Henrietta first. She immediately reported that she had been taking care of Belinda when she took her first steps. I tried to imagine how she had shown that in her drawings, when she unrolled a piece of paper. The week materialized as a montage of events and objects. Some of the drawings clearly represented activities, others needed Henrietta's interpretation. A smiling cow with its calf was how she depicted Stephen's compliment on her work at the farm. A table with coffee and a cake showed that her mother had been surprised and pleased by her preparing a snack for her when she came home from work one evening. Overall the work was a delight. It showed Henrietta's seriousness, but also her subtle humour and imagination.

Suddenly the smile disappeared from her face. 'When my parents are so kind and we start to get on better, I get scared they'll start talking about my going back to work again. That they'll try to persuade me.'

I told Henrietta that she should draw another picture in the coming week, and go on getting to know Belinda. If her parents tried to discuss work with her, she should simply tell them she wasn't ready for that yet. The most important thing now was to continue what she and I had started.

After Henrietta went out, her parents entered, and they immediately expressed their worry about Henrietta's work situation. The doctor had given her sick leave and the florist was being very understanding, but 'How long is this going to go on?' they wanted to know.

Tora was afraid that Henrietta would end up like the young people she saw without work, hanging around street corners, picking up boys, taking drugs. She saw the cheap magazines Henrietta read as a step in that direction. Stephen differed. He believed Henrietta's background was good enough to keep her out of that sort of trouble, but he thought it should soon be decided if she would return to work or not.

'I understand that you're both worried about Henrietta and her job. I think we all recognize how serious her situation is. I can also guess that you are concerned with how she spends her time. For it is just now that she is preparing for her future. And that is serious work.

'At this point, she needs to know she has the support of her family. So that when she takes on her occupation and starts to think about making her own way in the world, she'll have a strong foundation beneath her. You have given that so far. As Stephen said, she does an honest job on the farm and, even if she hated the florist shop, they value her sufficiently to hold her place open for her now. The best you can do now is to continue being the good solid parents Henrietta knows you to be.

'Tora, you can continue to enjoy your daughters, and their development, and appreciate that Henrietta is growing into the big sister role for Belinda, loving her and helping to take care of her. I know that you are worried, and that's quite OK. As a mother it's natural that you feel it and express it as clearly as you do. I still think that if you are irritated with Henrietta's lack of tidiness, you should be more specific and explicit about what you expect of her.

'The same is true for you Stephen. If you want help with the harvest, you should tell Henrietta that you're hoping she'll join you as she has earlier.' That was no problem at all, he answered, because he really wanted her to come.

When Henrietta came in the fourth time, she declared that she wanted to quit her job. She was tired of avoiding old schoolmates and friends of her parents, who asked about her work situation. She had started helping out at the farm. The work there gave her a lot of satisfaction and she reported proudly that both Stephen and his parents were glad to have her back again.

'How are you going to tell them you're going to quit?'

Henrietta planned to break the news over dinner on Friday. That was the night her mother didn't work and everyone was home. Then on Monday she would go to town and tell them at the shop that she would not return.

'Then you've got work enough ahead of you. Only I want you to go on drawing the good things that happen. You have really started them happening now!'

There was a pause after Tora and Stephen came into my office and sat down. Tora started to speak several times, then stopped herself. After an encouraging glance and gesture from Stephen, she finally began.

She said she had been thinking very much about Henrietta and her life. She regretted very much Henrietta's childhood, that she hadn't had enough time to be a good mother to her. She described, for the first time, how she had been a single mother in the early years of Henrietta's childhood. Because her first husband was extremely irresponsible, it had been up to her to raise and support her family, as much when she was married as after the divorce. She had been alone four years — so Henrietta was 6 — when Tora met Stephen and life felt as if it started again.

'Henrietta must see now how much she ought to have had as a child. And what I couldn't give her. She must resent that. I can't help thinking that jealousy must be some part of what she's doing now since she can see how much love and attention the baby gets. She must see now how much she missed.'

I told her that, in knowing Henrietta as well as I did, I imagined she appreciated whatever they had together during her childhood. I never had any sense from Henrietta that she blamed or resented her mother. Quite the opposite . . . .

'Still,' she persisted, 'it's not so strange for her to feel jealous over her little sister.'

Stephen broke in at this point to say this last bit was nonsense, since Henrietta was more involved with Belinda, and spent more time with her than either of them over the past weeks.

Tora shrugged. 'But neither she nor I gained as much from each other as we should have.' This was followed by silence.

Then Stephen returned to the question of work. He thought by now it should be clear whether or not Henrietta was going back to the florist shop. She had started helping at the farm and he thought this was wrong while she was on sick leave. I upheld the earlier stance that Henrietta had to be the one to initiate discussion about her future.

'Even if you think it's too much for her to tackle on her own, you must wait 'til she makes her start, 'til she makes up her own mind. She has to learn from experience that she is responsible for the choices she makes, and that she is answerable herself for those choices. It's something she has to learn on her own, you know that. And you know too that you can only support her, even if it's hard not to want to do more at a time like this.'

I redirected the discussion to wonder if the two of them had much opportunity to be alone together, to do things — the two grown-ups together. They were not sure what I meant, but because of their work schedules, and the children, they didn't think they did. It was not anything they felt need of.

'Perhaps it's too much to think about?'

Tora smiled a little and hinted that perhaps Stephen no longer wanted to be alone with her. She didn't know. Stephen said a farmer couldn't toy with nature. First, the harvest had to be brought in, then some buildings needed repairing. There simply was no time to relax before Christmas was on them.

'I wasn't thinking so much of relaxation, but rather that the children might benefit from sometimes being on their own. They might better appreciate the time you do give them, and appreciate themselves better somehow. Well, some couples need time for themselves. But since it seems impossible for you to make this sort of time, perhaps we'd better drop the subject.'

By the next session Henrietta had informed her parents and employer of her decision to quit. She felt relieved and could finally enjoy the farm work and her friends there with a clear conscience. It was funny, though, she added, that quitting that job made her think about her future.

'I think that's pretty sensible for a young woman of 18. Have you got any ideas yet?'

Farm work was always a possibility — that was a field she knew well. She considered working as a veterinary nurse, or as a veterinarian's assistant. A zoo would be exciting, but she recognized there was little possibility for work of that sort in Denmark. She thought, though, that working around animals was something she could see herself doing for a long time.

'It's not so illogical, your interest in animals, given the work you've done with plants and gardening. Have you discussed any of this with Stephen?'

'Sure. He thinks it's right that I could be a good farmer. And that a vet's assistant is a good career, but he said the zoo thing sounded insecure. He said it was a funny idea, but he didn't laugh at it though.'

'What do you think of what he said?'

'I think he's probably right.'

'Hmmm. That's fine then. And now that it's the autumn, you can take your time to find out about training and openings. You really have time to think about what comes next. I know that time to think is important to you. And it looks like you're starting to make some pretty good choices, Henrietta.

'I can't see that there are any more problems now, so I don't believe we need to meet again after today. Is that OK with you? Fine.

'But I do want to ask you if you'll try something else at home. I know you've started making coffee for your mother when she comes home from work, and you help out quite a lot now with Belinda — or at least your parents say so. Just once or twice in the next week, I wonder if you can find something that will really please and surprise your parents. It'll probably be something to do with housework, but I'm sure you know best what it will be. One of your parents might be shocked, then, or joke about it. (It's the way adults can behave when teenagers surprise them. They often have trouble receiving.) But then you should just behave as if it's natural, nothing to discuss at all. What do you think of that?' She smiled at me, and I wished her good luck and asked her to send her parents in to me now.

As they filed into my office, Tora and Stephen looked more relaxed than previously. Stephen said that by now I probably knew it, but Henrietta had announced that she was quitting her job over Friday dinner, and that she went down to the florist shop and cleared it all up herself. He expressed some surprise and pride that she didn't ask for any help doing this.

'Well, quitting jobs doesn't seem to make her less messy. I'd like to know what happens next?!' Tora complained.

I leaned conspiratorially near Tora. I looked her fully and earnestly in the eye. 'Look, I've tried to be encouraging and perhaps that was a mistake. I'll be perfectly frank. At this stage — from what I know of teenagers I've worked with here — I think you can expect that this untidiness thing will only get worse. We can hope it won't get much worse, but she has to get a bit older, to mature a bit, before she changes. I know this is hard to swallow, but perhaps if you are prepared you may not be so disappointed.'

The final meeting with Henrietta's parents, a week later, was a brief one. Stephen reported that he had helped find Henrietta a full-time position as a farm-hand with a fair salary and room and board. She would move down there at the end of the month.

'And,' added Tora, 'I have to tell you that your advice was wrong. She's actually begun to help out at home.'

I looked down at my hands, then up at Tora. 'Well, I admit I like being proved wrong in that way. You and I probably agree, Tora, that we gain much more by expecting the worst from people than hoping for the best.

'That's why I think it's right, Stephen, to keep telling your wife there'll never be the opportunity for the two of you to spend time on your own.'

Brief therapy tenders a theory of change which can be seen here adapted to a case of adolescent attempted suicide. The problem presented in therapy was twofold. The immediate issue was the crisis of Henrietta's attempted suicide, to which was related the issue articulated in Stephen's introductory statement to the therapist and echoed throughout treatment: the parents' concern over Henrietta's social and employment situation.

Stephen's and — particularly — Tora's persistent disparagement of Henrietta's activities at home and attitude towards her job heightened her sense of failure and helplessness, and blocked her attempts to communicate her distress. What was no doubt intended as encouragement of healthy and active participation made it more difficult for her to behave as the young adult she was. She was of an age where she was ready to express her satisfaction or otherwise, and to ponder, plan and select a realistic alternative to a position she disliked. The therapist's aims were twofold. The first was to interrupt Henrietta's cycle of dissatisfaction and the activities which perpetuated the sense of desolation she described at work and at home. The second was to alter the family interactions which contributed to the crisis. This was important since they threatened to crystallize this event into an integral element of family dynamics.

The first part of the intervention addressed Henrietta's immediate source of dejection. The whole issue of the florist shop was reframed as subservient to the earnest business of the work she faced in therapy. There were 'a lot more serious things to worry about now'. The homework tasks demanded that she observe her environment in a new way and that she express her observations in a form that excited her aesthetic talents. She was encouraged to challenge conditions imposed on her by others. This was a difficulty which came through her description of her work place. She also revealed that she avoided confrontations at home, by slipping off to her room. The instruction not to respond to parents' enquiries about work sanctioned experimentation of ways to express her own needs positively. Her tendency to shirk encounters which demanded opposition or restraint was offset by the directive to observe the effects of her father's openly expressed irritation on other family members, and contrast these to her own response. The task to observe and record 'good things' pictorially was inspired by an earlier experience of the therapist. The approach, however, matched Henrietta's initial presentation of self as rather younger than her years, and her style of taking time for herself to sit quietly thinking. The naivety of her task demanded that Henrietta restructure her perceptions of each day into agreeable form. It shifted her attention to a creative enterprise, away from her preoccupation with failure.

The second set of directives proposed to alter problem-maintaining interactions in the family by strategic means. A primary aim was to acknowledge and uphold the previous and present efforts of the parents in raising their children. Successful resolution of crisis is related to the succour of significant others (Eckenrode and Gore 1981; Hirsch 1981; Schneider 1981). At crisis events such as in this case, it becomes particularly important that parents do not withdraw their support for the 'offending' child. In many cases, crisis precipitates feelings in the parents of failure over their children's behaviour, or of being blamed by the child or by society. Parents may perceive themselves as incapable or unworthy of continuing in their role and seek to place their child in the hands of those who know better.

The job of the therapist is to sustain the parents as responsible, supportive, stable adults for their child when he or she most needs them. Practically, this aim took a rather repetitive and simple form with Tora and Stephen. Reframing was the fundamental skill employed as the therapist repeatedly encouraged Tora's anxieties as maternal and natural. Past parenting was interpreted as satisfactory in view of

97

Henrietta's amiable manner and the merit she earned from her employer. Tora's proposed theories of madness were ignored rather than tackled. The therapist avoided trying to convince the parents of Henrietta's capabilities. Instead, Tora was goaded to get after Henrietta to do her household tasks. Her behaviour was therefore regarded in the light of normal teenager–parent dispute over participation in housework, rather than as irregular or peculiar.

Stephen was urged, in a low-key fashion, to become more involved with Henrietta. The reader will note that differences in parental perceptions of Henrietta, and ideas about how to manage her, were not taken up as a conflict by the therapist. The father was 'merely' encouraged to articulate and demonstrate his appreciation of Henrietta's work and his somewhat pragmatic (as opposed to fearful or pathological) view of the problem. The outcome was that he helped Henrietta to find a position to move out to, one appropriate for a healthy young adult (cf. Haley 1980).

The third set of interventions was devised in response to the cross-generational involvements, and the apparent difficulties the family entertained in passing from one stage of the family life-cycle to the next. Clues to this therapeutic issue distinguished themselves early in treatment. Tora and Stephen defined Henrietta's suicide attempt with reproaches about her general behaviour. This problem formulation, Henrietta's age and her immature self-presentation, combined with her statement about her parents never listening to what she said, signalled difficulties over Henrietta's transition from a well-behaved teenager to a responsible young adult.

This set of interventions was initiated early in treatment, when the therapist began meeting Henrietta and her parents separately. Defining the 'present issue' as the most important one (as opposed to seeking causation for the suicide attempt), the therapist worked individually with Henrietta to underscore the validity of her interests and activities and judgements: to foster her efforts to plan and choose for herself how the next stage of her life would be. Development of the big-sister role meant behaving more responsibly in the home, though it was never defined that way. Nor was her final task conceptualized in terms of responsibility, but rather as surprising her parents.

The therapist used the parents' worry to restrict the question of Henrietta's job to the therapeutic domain in order to interrupt the sequence of their badgering her over the issue at home. In the face of Tora's alternating pattern of overinvolvement (anxiety, guilt at not being a good mother, seeking ways to comprehend Henrietta's sickness) and underinvolvement (rejection and isolation of Henrietta as a sick person, criticism of her activities and friends, concentration on her younger sister), the therapist reframed Tora's complaints from one field of transaction to another. The difficulties of being mother to a growing teenager were stressed. The practical matters — housework,

98

having to miss work because of a sick family member, having to care for both a very young child and a troublesome teenager — were repeatedly discussed as worthy of serious attention.

The suggestion that the parents might discover more time for each other stems from the common family therapy notion that in families where one or both adults are overinvolved with a child, they tend to be underinvolved with each other. Here, Tora's response indicated this might be a relevant observation. The therapist's comments imply that Tora might benefit from attempts to attract more of Stephen's attention.

Dramatic acts such as Henrietta's can precipitate a set of responses which mark a young person for life: labelled, institutionalized, rejected within the family system. Long-term analytic psychotherapy with young persons may have benefits, although O'Connor in an illustrative defence of brief therapy, cites evidence from studies of obsessive–compulsive disorders in young people which suggests that analytic treatment is less than effective:

> in a six-year follow-up of obsessive–compulsive children, . . . seven out of ten still suffered from obsessive–compulsive symptoms. In addition, *all* former patients reported continued serious problems with social life and peer relationships. Most of these cases had been treated with intensive psychotherapy for an average of 17.7 months, once or twice weekly. (O'Connor 1983, p. 201, from Hollingsworth, Tanguay, Grossman and Pabst, *J of Am. Acad. Child Psychiat.*, 19, 134–144, 1980).

Henrietta was not obsessive–compulsive, but her action might well have led her into orthodox analytic psychotherapy, or a course of psychopharmocological treatment. She and her parents were seen five and six times respectively, over a period of just under six weeks, following her suicide attempt. To now, Henrietta has continued with the farm placement Stephen obtained for her. She is still in Laegernes Hus' catchment area. The last time she came to the clinic was for an examination and prescription for birth control.

Notes

1 The law was changed in 1986 so that joint custody is now possible under citation circumstances.

2 The pattern is not unknown in divorce cases. One patient came home to find his wife drinking coffee with a young woman. When he asked his wife who the visitor was, she turned red and looked speechlessly at the visitor. 'I'm afraid I have to tell you that I am a solicitor. I'm here to serve you a writ for a divorce.' It was news he had never heard from his wife.

3 In the hours when Laegernes Hus is closed, and over weekends, there is always a GP on duty to meet patients at the clinic, or to make house calls. It has evolved as general policy that when a crisis occurs at the home of a patient — attempted suicide, violence against a family member, sudden death, symptoms perceived as reaction to a recent crisis (such as a heart attack soon after the funeral of a loved one) — the house call is not finished at diagnosis and treatment.

The doctor remains with the family or individual patient until she or he is satisfied that they have asked the questions they harbour, have had the opportunity to discuss what happened and how, to explore what they think the crisis meant, what fears remain, what additional information they might require to get through to the next meeting. The doctor will leave at the time that the family or patient can manage the situation. These 'crisis' house calls always end with one of the following:

(a) an appointment with the same GP at the clinic for the following day;
(b) an agreement that the family will ring or be rung by the psycho-therapist;
(c) an agreement or contract that the doctor will return to visit the family either the next day, or at some point in the coming week.

6 Using experience

Petra

A physical disability can temporarily disrupt an individual's contribution to the community. Inappropriate intervention at such a point can render a useful person passive by reinforcing the disability, and removing the sense of being worthwhile and of use to anyone. One visit to Petra was enough for me to see that she was in a risk situation. She balanced on the edge between active confrontation of life and her natural concern for others, and becoming an aged patient, to be restrained and retained by others.

One day at the conference one of the doctors asked me to visit Petra, an old woman who lived in a nearby town. She had lost her husband three years before. Eighteen months after his death, she was discovered to have a cancer, after which followed a colostomy. Now she was 69, and just a year had passed since the death of her only daughter.

Petra had home-made cakes and fresh coffee ready for my visit. We talked at first about how nice it was where she lived. She had a cosy little house filled with lovely things obviously collected over the years. The little house had a pretty little garden, and her neighbours lived in close range. As we chatted she began weeping quietly. She paused and said finally, 'But how does all this help me when I cannot appreciate it any longer?'

I asked her to tell me what had happened. She said it began when her husband became sick. He had to lie in bed most of the time. 'He was so alert and alive,' she said. 'He couldn't move himself from his bed, but with my help he could sit in a chair for a few hours. It was that chair he sat in.' She pointed to a chair by the window. I walked over and put my hand on the back of the chair. From the window I could see the garden, and the road by which people passed. Petra's husband was able to watch people on their way to town, and also see them approaching his own front door.

'We lived for eight months in this way, from February through October. Then he grew weaker and weaker, and in the middle of October, I had to let them take him to hospital. I couldn't take proper care of him at home any longer. He was simply too weak.' She paused. 'He died a week later. We always stuck together, and he meant an awful lot to me. It was so difficult for me to see him so weak and helpless. And a short time after his death, they found a cancer, and then I had a colostomy.' She had asked the surgeon if it was cancer. He told her it was, but that they had taken away everything bad. She shouldn't have any further problems as long as she could cope with the little bags. 'And they weren't really any trouble to me.'

The pride in her voice reminded me how her generation had lived in a time when hot water and the freedom that cleanliness means were not a matter of course.

Next she told how her daughter had been examined for something in her legs. They had immediately sent her to hospital. From the local hospital, they rushed her to a big clinic where they removed one of her lungs. They sent her home again, saying that she was now well, and could continue as if nothing had happened. 'From the moment she told me she wasn't going to have further treatment, I knew what they told her wasn't true. I knew she didn't have a long time left. But I couldn't tell her that.'

First, Ethel had difficulties in walking. After she lost her sense of balance and began falling, she herself saw that she was going to die. At that point she and Petra began to talk about it. Petra moved from her little home into her daughter's household. In describing that time, she spoke of the many hours sitting by Ethel's bedside talking with her. Ethel had to take a lot of pills — almost forty each day — and a large part of Petra's day was spent dissolving the pills and preparing them for Ethel to take. 'She was so weak by that time that swallowing any food or liquid was a real effort for her. I think we both knew that there was no point to it, but . . . .

'My son-in-law couldn't talk to her — he didn't want to talk to her about it. Perhaps that was the most difficult part for her.'

Ethel and her husband had no children. Petra helped in their home until four days before Ethel's death, when she had to let them take her to hospital. Ethel was 48 when she died.

Petra had promised her daughter that she would help her son-in-law Harald when Ethel was not there any longer. 'I don't know where I got all the strength from. I was newly operated on myself. And I have never been fantastically strong. But somehow I got the strength to deal with it.' Petra stayed and helped Harald sell the hardware business he built up together with Ethel. He couldn't imagine going on with it alone. Petra did not move back into her little house until he obtained a new job in another city, and the new owners were able to work the business on their own. That was just a year ago.

'When I moved back here alone, I began thinking how meaningless it all seemed. And now I keep asking myself why did it happen that way? Why should she die and not you? She had so much life left. Their business had just reached a point where they could hire someone to help, and begin to travel and do the things they always looked forward to.

'I don't know . . . I don't know what I should do to get over it. I can see that it's unjust to my son, and to his wife. They can't understand it. They ask "Don't we mean anything to you?" I can't explain to them why I don't want to live any longer. They try to get me to go out, visiting them and their children and other people. But I can't pull myself together to do it. And the times when I try, I have to go home early. I can't listen to what they're saying, or really follow what's going on. It's just too much effort to do it.'

I asked if she would tell me about her life. Her father died when she was eight, and when her mother died four years later, Petra was sent to a household where she could work and live. It wasn't that they weren't good to her, but they weren't her family and didn't pretend to be. Her real brother and sisters were much older. They were each of them married and had their own homes, but none of them offered Petra a place when their mother died. Her only contact with any of them was an occasional day off or a holiday spent in one of their homes.

When she was 17 Petra met her husband in the Christmas season. They had talked so enthusiastically on the train where they met, that she forgot to get off at her stop. They married soon after. The man she married was ten years older than she. He owned a large farm he had inherited from his father, and so Petra moved in and learned to be a farmer's wife. The couple, who later had a son and a daughter, worked happily together with their family on the farm for many years.

Petra and Ethel had been very close from the start. As soon as the girl was old enough she helped with the chickens and the eggs, and feeding the baby pigs. Petra proudly described the business they developed together, with the eggs and the hens. It was a real contribution to the family economy. It was quite natural that Ethel stay and work with her mother until the time she met her husband and moved with him to another town. Nor was it unusual for Petra to visit her daughter's home, helping out in their business throughout the years. She had always felt welcome there, both by Ethel and by Harald.

Not many years after both children married and moved away, the couple sold the farm and bought the little house where she now lived alone.

As she told her story, I heard what Petra believed, but probably never said aloud. Her brother and sisters had abandoned her, and her husband was the first person who really chose her. I could also hear the special place her daughter held in her life. Ethel was the first human being Petra felt belonged to her, and to whom she belonged.

In her own assessment, Petra believed she recovered so quickly after her husband's death because she was obliged to take care of herself on her own. She related with some pride how the hospital instructor sent to help her after the colostomy, really did no work with her. In fact, she used to bring Petra her new patients and asked her to show them how to handle the bag and care for themselves at home.

Petra paused, then confided that she had just recently developed a new problem. She guessed it might be because she did not eat regularly now — sometimes didn't eat at all — but there was a problem of air passing into the bags. It was yet another reason she didn't want to go out. She was very afraid of smelling bad and offending someone. She quickly added that even if she did not want to eat every day, she always prepared food for herself. Her not eating was a question of appetite, not a lack of energy or effort.

When she stopped talking, I told her that her story told me not only about herself, but also something about life. I said it was very important that she had her freedom to go on crying, and not think that she had to ignore or avoid her feelings because of her children or anyone else. I said I thought it could be very important for her to sit down and remember and reflect on all that had happened in her life, especially the birth, growing up, and death of her daughter.

It was clear that she was a person able to teach others. The crises she had come through were not unusual, but the way in which she managed them was a lesson to others about how they might use their strengths in meeting difficult times. She had done this when her instructor brought other patients to her home.

Petra believed. 'If I can help others so that they won't have to live through the difficulties I've been through in the past year and a half, I'll do it. You know, I need help too — to get the most possible from the time I still have left with the people in my future.'

I next called in at Petra's little house after returning from my vacation. I visited her with a plan in the back of my mind. Old people have a very special way of showing when they are coming back to life after a difficult time. It's too much to say they look healthier, but there's something in their eyes and in their movements. Their overall manner communicates that, again, they have a right to be listened to. They have something to offer.

So it was with Petra. And I revealed my plan to her. Since my return from vacation, I had met a man in his fifties whose 23-year-old daughter had just died. The man was a widower, and had no other children. 'I want to bring this man to you. I believe that he might learn from your experience. Could I do that, Petra?'

She smiled at the cake as she cut me a second slice. 'Well, I am glad you had an enjoyable vacation, but I'm certainly pleased that you are back. Since your first visit, I have been looking forward to the time when you would bring someone here, whom I could help as much as you helped me.'

A significant factor in Petra's story was the action in the wings. Her son and his wife were occupied with the particulars of Petra's declining health. They saw her distracted social behaviour as proof of degenerating mental capacity. They had been to the clinic to discuss her 'condition' with one of the GPs. They wondered if an experienced professional would advise institutionalization, either now or in the near future. The Laegernes Hus doctors and I agreed on physical and psychosocial grounds that Petra was much better off in her own home.

I rang Petra at one time for her opinion on another case, to find this brave lady in tears. I drove by her house later that day. Her daughter-in-law had visited her earlier the same day. 'She won't let me do anything. She insists that I sit tight and not exert myself. I feel in myself that I am as healthy as I can be, but whenever she visits I'm plagued with doubts. Perhaps she knows something I don't, or maybe the doctor has told my son and her something he hasn't told me.'

The pressures on Petra dramatize the gravity of situations where people are perceived as no longer capable of using their knowledge and experience.

Recent studies of social support systems identify participation in social networks as an aspect of the 'ecological formulation' (Hirsch 1981, p. 162) vital for psychosocial well-being, and as contributory to the coping process of medical patients (Cobb 1979; DiMatteo and Hays 1981; Eckenrode and Gore 1981; Hirsch 1981; Lynch 1977; Tolsdorf 1976; Wellman 1981). The point of Petra's story is not that everyone must use all their strengths or experiences all the time. What is advocated is that the worker in an open community setting be alert to the abilities and resources people have. The option for Petra was a life where experiences become vicarious, where others employ their abilities and knowledge in caring, and where activity takes the form of memories and photographs on a bedside table.

The story illustrates three basic therapeutic principles at work. First, giving permission — actually prescribing — the patient to feel or be what they are. Secondly, a creative use of the past. Patients with gnawing doubts or guilt about the past are frequently instructed to consider and evaluate what they try unsuccessfully — and often obsessively — to forget. Requiring self-examination, contemplation and some kind of conceptual ordering of the past cuts through the pernicious pattern by demanding behaviour that the patient believes she cannot control or cease (Fisch *et al.* 1982). It can further alter perceptions of the present and the future, and as such has potential as a creative problem-solving method.

And third, asking Petra's help with other patients was a particularly good employment of this woman's resources. It was clear that her sense of self-worth came from the way she related to others. Her life story showed how she repeated this pattern throughout her life (Henry 1973; Wellman 1981). Petra was not yet in the position that bedridden or dying patients encounter, of being forced to be on the receiving end, unable to reciprocate. For the physicians and psychotherapist alike, there was no doubting her ability to survive physical and social stresses, and no need to subject her to incapacitation before absolutely necessary.

Not a Total Loss
Unlike Petra, Carl's position was not so much imposed upon him, but was rather the consequence of his life-style. But his story demonstrates how the worker may have to defend the opportunity of the patient to put his experience to use.

Grete's visit influenced my work with divorcing families more than anything else I can recall. Grete's mother had taken her and her two younger brothers, and moved out of their home to some relatives at the time when the threat of violence from their father became too great. I had worked with that couple months before without any real success, but when Grete began awakening, screaming in the nights, her mother sent her to talk with me.

Grete said the night the family fled from their home, she had said such nasty things to her father that she couldn't ever repeat them. She would only admit that she had said she hated him for what he had done to her and to her mother. Now she dreamed every night that he caught up with her on a street in the town, and demanded that she take back what she said. She was so frightened that she literally would not walk in the streets. She had begun taking small back pathways. These took her a longer time, but meant her father would not see her if he happened to be driving through town. The nights when she woke screaming, she always dreamed that he caught her on one of the small pathways.

I told Grete that if I should be able to help her, she had to go home and tell her mother it was necessary that they all five came together, including her ex-husband. Ever since Grete, I have determined to try as hard as possible to meet children with both parents at the time of separation or divorce, preferably before the split, but afterwards if that is all that is possible. It is not easy for the children. The parents often argue against it. And it is hard work for the therapist. But clinical experience suggests that this work makes a qualitative difference in the way these children are able to establish relationships with both parents, even if they do not live together any longer.

So when Irene rang for an appointment to help sort out her separation from Carl, I repeated that I wanted the whole family to come.

Nearly everybody in town knew about Carl's alcohol problem. It was accepted that Carl drank too much. But since he was such a good house painter, people didn't mind. On the contrary, serving him beers was an easy way to show appreciation for his work. Irene told me over the telephone that she had decided it had to stop. This last time Carl had been found unconscious in the street. She could no longer bear to have her children humiliated because of their father.

106

They all looked very ill at ease when they came into the first session. Irene looked squarely and intently at me. It was as if, were she to allow herself to look to one side or the other, she might be distracted from her decision. Marlene, who was 13, had the righteous look of a teenage girl who has seen her mother give her father too many chances, and who has seen her father fail many times. She sat watching, waiting for me to begin. Brian, who was 8, sat uneasily on the chair. He did not know who to look at, and he looked from his mother to his father to me, then round again. Carl sat looking at the floor. He had the lean, wiry body of a labourer — hard-working rather than healthy in the impression it gave. His face betrayed the ravages of the alcohol he had consumed over the years.

I began by asking Carl if they had all talked at home together before coming. He said, 'No.' He had only talked with Irene. I asked the children if either mother or father had spoken with them. Marlene said yes, that her mother had talked with her. Brian said he wasn't sure why they were there. Mother only told him to come with them. I asked Brian if his mother had told him anything, and he said he couldn't remember.

'But I told you . . . ' Irene began to interrupt. I stopped her and asked Marlene to explain to Brian why they were there today. Marlene looked at her mother, then said to Brian, 'It's because the two of them want to divorce now.' I asked Brian if he understood what Marlene said. He started wriggling in his seat, and giggling. He didn't know which way to look. I repeated my question, if he knew what it meant that they were going to divorce. Brian continued giggling and still did not answer.

Irene leaned over to Brian and said he knew what that meant. 'You know Charles' parents don't live together any more. And sometimes Charles lives with his mother, and sometimes he lives with his father.' Brian sat quietly on his chair now. It was obvious that he was listening to what was going on, but also that he was quite scared.

I asked Marlene what it meant to her that her parents were going to get divorced. She said she didn't think it would mean anything special. They would all live in the same town, and she could see her father when she wanted to. From the way she spoke, I could hear that Irene had talked to her about that.

Carl looked at the floor. He still had not said anything. I asked him if he agreed that the children should stay with Irene, and then be able to visit him. He raised his head slowly for the first time, and said that with his working hours, nothing else was realistic. He spoke in a low monotone, but he said very clearly that the most important thing for him was that the children go on living with their mother in the house where they grew up. He wanted them to have their own rooms and to suffer as little change as possible. He wanted them to go on as a family. When he finished speaking, he looked down at the floor again.

I told him I could see how difficult it must be for him to say what he had just said. The whole situation must be very difficult for him. For the first time he looked directly at me. He did not say anything, but he looked back down again. I asked if he wanted to add anything more, but he only shook his head.

'This is a very difficult situation for your father. He knows how he has lived these years, and he knows that now your mother is serious in wanting to divorce him. She doesn't want to live together with him any more. He feels very guilty about the two of you. It's very hard to have such guilt feelings about the children you love and feel you've hurt so much.'

Brian started rattling his chair again. Irene told him it was not necessary to move about like that. It wasn't as bad as I described, she said, and there was no reason for making the children unhappy. At that, Brian's eyes filled with tears. 'I'm so sorry for Father,' he said when I asked why he was crying. He sniffed loudly.

I asked Marlene what she was thinking. She replied she could only think about how hard it had been for her mother over the years.

'But I'm going to miss Daddy,' Brian said.

'Do you know where you'll be able to see Daddy after he's moved?' I asked. 'Have you planned where you'll be and whether you'll spend time with the children after you've moved out, Carl?'

Carl still looked at the floor. 'I don't know what to do about it, but I am afraid of losing touch with them.'

'How would you describe your relation to your children now?' He only looked at the floor, and when he did not answer, I asked, 'What do you do with Marlene, for instance?'

He thought for a few moments, then he looked up and at Marlene. 'We never do anything.' It was as if he had thought of it for the first time.

'So now you do nothing together. Well, it's a point to start from.

'Marlene, can you think about how it will be when you see your father in the future — about what would you like to do with him?' Marlene looked shocked at my question, and drew in her breath audibly.

Irene interrupted with the information that the first five years of Marlene's life, Carl had mostly worked abroad. That was why he and Marlene didn't have much of a relationship now. It would be hard for Marlene to answer my question.

I stopped Irene sharply, and pointed out that my purpose was to try to discover what relationship existed between Marlene and Carl, or what might be developed. From now on, Marlene and Carl's relationship was their own concern.

I wanted Irene to stay quiet while we worked on that. I asked Carl if he could think of possible things to do together with Marlene. He couldn't imagine anything. He didn't know what to do with her.

'That's fine, then,' I said. 'Now at least we know where we're going to begin. And that's very important.' After checking with them the date and plans for Carl's departure, his new address, and the like, I told Carl and Brian and Marlene to think seriously about the future. 'I want the three of you to talk together about what you think about the future. We'll discuss this at the very beginning of the next session.

'Thank you all for coming. Ah . . . before you go I want to warn you that in the next week you may be unhappy at times — or sometimes feel very angry. You might find it difficult to concentrate on your work or at school with your friends. Try not to let this worry you too much. Things can be that way at difficult times. And you are all in a very difficult period just now, I know that.'

I began the second session by asking how the tasks went. Brian quickly responded with something about football matches. I looked at Carl. He said that Brian had come to him, and asked if the two of them might go to a football match once Carl had left. Carl thought it was a very good idea. He said then that he didn't want to trouble the boy, but he had been thinking about how much he would miss his story-telling with Brian. Carl used to sit up and read or tell stories to Brian on the evenings they were home alone. 'But what would stop you from keeping to that each time he visits you?' Carl looked at me a little shocked: 'Well, nothing. I just didn't think of that.'

Marlene answered that she had not spoken with her father at home. She added diffidently that she wanted him to teach her something of his painting skills. Carl, it turned out, was one of those house painters who is also a fine picture painter, though he never mentioned this to anyone. Carl didn't know if he was good enough to teach her, but he looked pleased and said he was willing to try.

Carl was to move into his new flat in the coming week, so we finished with his making separate dates with both children to visit his new home, and elaborating some plans as to how they would spend that time together.

During this discussion, Irene squirmed uneasily in her seat. When it drew to a close, she came out with what she was unhappy about. 'You're trying to divide the children so that they don't know where they belong!' she said to me. 'You'll split them into two by doing it!' After having spent many years in a disappointing relationship, it is not unusual for a spouse to react when they see their children planning good times with the departing parent. Still, such responses provide an opportunity to let both parents know just what they are up to.

'Up to this moment you have been two parents, and have given your children a father and mother. Because the two of you decided that you cannot go on living together, it's no reason to take away one of their parents. Children will always have both a father and a mother, and it is your responsibility to let them feel they really have both.'

'But . . .'

'There are no buts about it. You have decided to divorce and you must take responsibility for the consequences of that decision.'

I generally do not ask about feelings in divorce work. I do try to reframe or teach from them when they surface. Perhaps more importantly, the aim is to be straight and direct and if necessary severe with parents who continue their disagreements through their children or through other means. Grete's mother, for example, had offered to continue doing her ex-husband's washing and ironing.

Participants in divorce groups repeatedly report difficulties in arranging practicalities in the early stages following separation. It is not unusual for individuals either to make enormous irrational demands, or, conversely, to give away parental or material rights which they later regret or attempt to renegotiate (Krantzler 1975; Weiss 1975).

Where a couple express their need or desire to work on decisions related to their separation, or to resolve or to close some of the issues at the heart of their relationship, then sessions can be devoted to that kind of work (cf. Oberg and Oberg 1982). But when a couple is at the stage of disintegration seen in this family, attempted resolution of feelings can be detrimental to the individuals and the agreements they have reached. It is therefore especially important that in divorce work the purpose of each session is clear to the family members and to the therapist.

The third session was our last all together. The purpose of this session was to follow up Carl's dates with the children, and to check with the couple whether they had particular difficulties straightening out details of economy, the household, and common objects. In Carl and Irene's case there was little problem. Where couples persistently refuse to agree or draw this business to a close, I arrange to see them as a twosome to work with them to complete the details of parting.

Unless a couple have severe problems in splitting, I generally see them three or four times with their children. I often see the non-custodial parent for a follow-up session some weeks or months after the separation. When I saw Carl, six weeks after this last family session, we discussed how it was for him to live on his own. Teaching Marlene about painting was not easy — she was often grouchy or eager to rush off somewhere else. But his preparations for the teaching had renewed his interest in art. When I asked him about Brian, he grinned shyly. Carl admitted that he was still drinking, but two days before the boy's visits, he would begin to dry out, so that he would be sober for the times the boy spent at his flat. And it went well for them together. I usually evaluate the past, to try to plan future goals in these follow-up sessions, but Carl resisted all my attempts. He did not yet want to think about any future.

Irene came back with the children after a month. With Marlene we discussed how it would be for a 13-year-old girl living with her mother and younger brother. The aim of this kind of discussion is to individualize all family members, and to try to prevent an older child taking over care of the parent. Marlene described how she was spending her time, and what activities she was engaged in at school. They discussed too how Brian and Marlene's relationship had altered (Minuchin and Fishman 1981).

These discussions can prove useful where children are reacting to their parents' separation, or where there is 'unfinished business' which they find too difficult to discuss with one of the parents. Brian and Marlene expressed no special problems at this time. But by meeting them in this follow-up, I made clear to them that they could return at any time, with any need.

With Irene I wanted to discuss how she was managing now that she no longer had to care for Carl. She had always had a part-time job, and now without Carl, and without the burden of his business, she discovered a leisure time. She had very many ideas of how she wanted to use it, and had already started a number of projects. We spoke about the use of time, her plans for herself in the near future, and perhaps in the years to follow, as the seed of an idea for her development as a woman in transition, in addition to her role as single mother.

Realistic support lies at the corner-stone of divorce work. The increased demand for this kind of work at Laegernes Hus testifies to the need people experience at time of separation or divorce. In this story, support takes different forms. For Carl it meant clarifying his new position as absent father, and helping him plan for the initial stages following the split. Specifically, this meant creating the possibilities for future contact with his children. For Irene, it meant limiting and reframing her responses to him, to enable her to allow her children to maintain a relationship with their father, despite a difficult history.

Anger is 'used' in session, but not in the conventional therapeutic or cathartic sense. Divorcing couples and their children frequently display anger and hurt. The therapist uses the force of these expressions to emphasize the consequences and responsibilities of separation. Similarly, anger can provide the base for planting hopes for qualitative changes in the future; as a drive in the fight for life ('so this won't happen in your life again . . . ').

It is known that individuals respond to critical loss, like divorce or death, at different paces. Therefore any two family members are likely to be at different reaction stages at a given moment (Krantzler 1975; Lindemann 1944). One task of the therapist is to uphold the prerogative of each family member to 'be' at whatever stage of reaction he is, and to acknowledge the signs and needs which each particular phase holds (Marris 1978). So that, for example, Brian is assured that it is quite OK to feel sorry for his Dad, even if nobody else in the

111

family does. Irene's response in these sessions is not unfamiliar. As she sees it, she suffered for years with Carl.

The therapist must recognize that children are often expected to ignore their own feelings and needs, feelings and needs which are the result of their parents' actions. The therapist has the task in these circumstances of sanctioning the reality of each individual's experience (Satir 1967; Watzlawick 1976). The goals of this sort of divorce work at Laegernes Hus have been:

1   To construct a plan and contract between each parent and each child. I work openly and explicitly with both the custodial parent and the non-custodial parent, to establish the time, place, and nature of the contact which will follow the separation. This generally involves practical discussion of when the leaving parent is to depart, and the possibilities which the new home or accommodation will provide — as well as enquiries about areas of shared interest, hopes, expectations between child and adult. If the parent has already left, I enquire about existing arrangements and agreements, to evaluate their nature and whether they are satisfactory for those involved.

   This discussion ends with dates between the non-custodial parent and individual offspring or sibling groups, where all are clear as to time of meeting, returning, and how the time together will be spent. In this study it is clear the sort of difficulties the non-custodial parent can have even imagining enjoyable contact with his children. Carl — and many parents like him — never think of asking their children how they would like to spend their visits together.

   Another reason for open planning stems from experience where sabotage from either parent can have negative consequences for the children. The therapist has to anticipate problems when negotiating these plans, in order to prevent them as far as possible.

2   To create positive expectations and opportunities for constructive contact and support between siblings. As family structure is altered at time of separation or divorce, the value of generational alliances becomes especially important. The potential of these alliances is suggested or highlighted by asking children

   (a) what they want to learn from one another in the time to follow. This question directs their attention from taking care of either parent, to relating more directly and constructively with one another;

   (b) what they enjoy doing, so that they can plan what activities they want to pursue or increase together. This is particularly important in the period of disorientation which typically follows close on the separation itself;

(c) what they would like to begin doing together. This question assumes parental separation to be a watershed for all family members. The reorganization of the household is defined as a starting-point for new activities and a new quality of contact between siblings (cf. Minuchin and Fishman 1981).

3   To set goals for the future. Discussion here often has the purpose of promising a future rather than clearly defining one, since families so near to separation tend to exhibit crisis responses which temporarily inhibit realistic planning. This discussion includes difficulties which family members anticipated or feared. It also includes identifying potential sources of support, hopes and dreams, and the problems of managing predictable reactions within self, and amongst relatives and community contacts (cf. Krantzler 1975 and Weiss 1975 for descriptions of the usefulness of this kind of discussion in divorce group settings).

It is well for the therapist to keep in mind, and in the foreground of discussions about the future where both partners are present, that issues which relate to the children may be of mutual concern, but that planning for the future is an individual and private matter for either adult.

The probability that one or the other parent will not show up for some appointment in the course of this work is worth noting. It is probably most useful to construe this behaviour in the context of different paces and modes of reaction to the crisis of separation.

This is one of the few circumstances which, for me, extenuates a broken appointment.

The experiences that Carl was encouraged to develop and put to use in his story are talents and interests which have lain dormant. 'Using Linda's Past' demonstrates how recycling symptoms can improve the quality of a family's function.

Using Linda's Past
When she rang for an appointment, Linda introduced herself by saying that she was looking forward to meeting me. She said that when she informed her therapy group that she was moving to our part of the country, her group leader told her that he had been on one of my courses. She started to describe how difficult it was leaving the group at that point. She had been in it for so long, and it was just beginning to help. I interrupted her by saying that I looked forward to seeing her with her family in the following week.

At the start of our first session, I asked them to tell me the reasons they came. Thomas, Linda's husband, started by clearing his throat and folding his arms, and replying in an earnest voice that there were two reasons — he glanced over to Linda — that there were three reasons, actually, for their coming just now. Some weeks after they had moved

113

to the area from Copenhagen, Thomas had some trouble with his stomach, and came to see one of the doctors at the clinic. He received a prescription, but at the same time the doctor talked about stress factors, and said that people with Thomas' type of ailment often found it useful to work with me. He paused and looked at Linda.

'He didn't tell me about that part of his examination until I mentioned the letter from our son's school. You see, we got a letter about George, our younger son, from the school doctor. He examined him, and recommended that we take George to our GP for a fuller check-up. Apparently, one of his teachers wondered about George's hearing. She said he was so quiet in class, and sometimes he didn't respond to what was asked.'

'Has one of the doctors seen him yet?'

'Yes,' Thomas answered. 'We brought him here a few days ago. But the doctor found nothing wrong with his hearing or his sight. He seems to be in perfect health.'

'Frankly,' said Linda, 'we don't understand it. George is not quiet or withdrawn at home.'

I paused for a moment, then looked at Thomas. 'And the third reason?'

'Yes, as I told you on the 'phone. My group therapist had been on one of your courses. He said that when it was time for me to have further treatment, I should remember him to you.'

'Oh.' I smiled at Linda, and nodded. I turned to George. 'Do you know what it's about, this school thing?'

'No. I don't understand it. I don't know anything about it. Nobody talked to me about it.' He sat on his chair and looked earnest and puzzled.

'Frankly, I'm a bit worried,' Linda said. 'I'm more than a bit worried that he might have somehow inherited my propensity for depression.'

'Yes,' said Thomas. 'Linda has had treatment for her depression on and off for the past 15 years. Early in our marriage she was admitted to a psychiatric ward. She had all the treatments possible there. And she's also been a day patient. She tried art therapy, and group therapy, and . . . '

'. . . And I have had three different kinds of individual therapy. One doctor even tried a diet treatment − he thought my depression might be caused by an allergy to food . . . '

'So,' I said. 'I can understand that you are worried about George.' I looked at George. The 12 year old blushed immediately but he did not answer.

'Well, you see and hear well enough, from what I can make out.'

'I don't know anyone at school yet. I'm just watching to see who I want to spend my time with.'

'OK. I'll talk with your teacher about it.' I paused for a moment, then looked at Andrew, who was 14, and asked him what he thought about it. I was referring to George's situation at school, but he answered that he was bored with tiptoeing around the house during his mother's depressions. He said that he couldn't listen to music, or watch TV, or bring home any of the new people he met at school. Even if he came home late, he was blamed for her being depressed, and he was fed up with it.

Andrew's response and the description of the family life during Linda's depressions greatly contrasted with the family's appearance. The overall impression the family gave was of cleanliness, freshly pressed, being upright, and alert. Even Andrew, at 14, was very much his own person, self-possessed and attentive. It was the kind of family you see in a restaurant, and think, 'How nice'.

'So now I know that Andrew wants something to be different, and so do your mother and father. What about you?' I asked, turning to 6-year-old Judith. 'What would you like?'

'I want a pony!' she proclaimed. 'They promised me a pony when we moved to the country.'

Thomas quietly assured her that she would get a pony. They simply hadn't had the time since they had moved: 'You know it takes more time to get a pony than a hamster.'

'From my work in families, I know there are places where you can be quite alone by yourself, if that's what you want. But you can always know that somebody will be able to help you if you are in difficulties. Is that the feeling you've got in your family too?' I looked around the family circle, at one after another. Each nodded solemnly. I told them it was encouraging to confirm the impression the session had given me: that they were a family ready to help whichever of them needed it.

'This week, I want you to try to help in a way I'll bet you haven't thought of before. What do you think of that?' They all nodded again. I looked at Linda. 'You moved into this area two months ago. I'll bet that with all the work involved in resettling, you have fought very hard not to give in to your depression. And sometimes you have lost that battle.' She nodded. 'Since I shall be seeing you in the next week, I think you'll be safe enough not to have to struggle so hard against it. When you feel your depression coming, let it come to you. Just let it come, as you know it will.

'Now, for the rest of you — I want each of you to say you'll help by doing what I ask you to. Will you do that? Good. Now, in the next week, each time you think that your mother, your wife, might be low or depressed, I want you to tell her how sad she looks, and tell her what things are depressing that day, what she might be depressed about. Is that clear? Do you think you can tell her things that are depressing?' I asked George. 'Fine!'

'And you, Thomas. I think it would be useful, given what your doctor said, if you could compile a list of the various factors you suspect contribute to any stress you might have now. Could you find time to do that between now and our next session? Fine!'

I began the second session by checking that everybody had done their task. George and Andrew looked at each other, and giggled a bit. All said that they had at least tried.

'Everybody has done that to help you?' I asked Linda.

'Well, they certainly told me enough depressing things. But I . . . '

'Fine. Good. Then they all did their job. It's not an easy task, but I was sure that you could all do it. And also you, Linda, you let yourself feel the feelings you had this week? Fine. Good.' Then I asked Linda what she was thinking of when she was depressed.

Linda sighed deeply. Then she started to tell how bad she felt as a wife and mother. How she was never able to do anything worthwhile, even if Thomas was so kind to her that he did not deserve a wife like her. Her children were so bright and attractive, yet when she looked at them, she felt as if she had given them nothing. She felt ashamed of her feelings and her life when she looked at them.

'"Why have I been put upon this earth?" That's the question that still returns. Then I have to go to bed.' She finished looking down at her hands which she was twisting in her lap.

I have developed a particular way of clearing my throat — it is rather a neutral sound, like a small earthquake, but I like to imagine it conveys a sense of comprehension to the person to whom it is directed. I use it when I don't want to prolong discussion, but still want the person to know I have caught the meaning of what they have said. As Linda wrung her hands expectantly, I made that sound. Then I turned to Andrew.

'What makes you feel worthwhile?'

Andrew said that he felt good when he was able to help with the cooking at home. He had learned to do that because his mother was often too depressed to cook the meals. When I asked if there was anything else, he said that he liked the people he knew. In Copenhagen, he used to visit an elderly housebound person. He had other older friends, and he seemed proud of the relationships he had with them.

George told how much he liked what he had done to his new room. Since they had moved to their new house, he had his own room for the first time. He had decorated it all himself. 'And he keeps me out!' Judith interrupted, and listed all the interesting things George had in his room: models, and pictures on the walls, and a special hamster palace.

'So you keep out of George's room when he asks you to? What else do you do that's good at home?' And Judith told how she helped Thomas lay the breakfast table most mornings.

'Fine. Thomas, since Linda has always worked at home, you have provided the financial support for the family. And you have helped Linda be depressed, which must have taken a lot of your time. Those are two very worthwhile things we know, but let's take a look at your list of stresses.'

The list was short and general. It was clear that for many years he had invested his energy in taking care of wife and children. It appeared he had forgotten how to acknowledge his own needs. I asked him what he did to get rid of the stress he collected. He answered that he didn't know, but he and I agreed that it was a serious ,issue for him and his health.

At the end of this session, I reminded Thomas of the seriousness of what we had discussed, and told him I wanted him to take 15 minutes every day when he came home from work: 15 minutes not more or less. In this time, he was to tell Linda everything that he could think was wrong or bad about her. He should think during the day what he would say to her — it could be things from the past, or the present. Or dumb things she might do in the future. Things she had done or said to him or to others. For 15 minutes each day. I asked him if he could do that, and he said he was quite sure he could. He looked earnest when he replied, and very thoughtful.

I told the children they had seen it was OK to tell mother when she looked depressed. Now we could work on stopping making her feel guilty by tiptoeing around the house.

'Judith, what did you say to your Mum when you saw she was depressed?'

She smiled charmingly. 'George won't let me in his room!' Linda interrupted to say that she had done a better job than that: 'I think it was Wednesday evening, after I had been watching the TV. I went into our bedroom, and discovered Judith on the floor with my jewellery box. All my jewellery was spread over the floor. She has been told many times not to touch it, and when she saw me standing in the door — my mouth must have been hanging open — she said, 'It's what the lady told me to do!'

We all laughed, and I repeated that they should not under any circumstances tiptoe around the house. And I told Linda that she should concentrate on feeling whatever she felt that week.

Linda began the third session by saying that she had had a terrible week. She felt down most of the days and had in fact to get out of bed to come to the session.

'I'm glad you say that,' I told her. 'It's quite normal — almost an expectation now — for people to have a bit of depression after the second or third session of family therapy. I was going to mention it at the end of last week, but I didn't want to put any pressure on you.

'So she had all of you working very hard. Did you keep to your tasks? It must have been very . . . how was it for you Thomas?'

Thomas told that he did not have anything else to bring up after the third day, and that it was really hard work to think of more to say or even things to make up. But he kept to his task, because he believed it would help.

117

'Fine.' We all sat back in our chairs, quiet for a minute or two. 'Linda,' I said finally, 'you have been in so many groups and growth experiences. Have you ever done any family sculpting?[1] No? Well . . . ' I explained the technique, and asked if she would sculpt how her depression benefited the family (Satir 1972).

We then discussed the sculpture all together. I told them how their family reminded me of another I knew once. The husband had had a very demanding job. He was tired when he arrived home from work each night, but rather than complain to his family, or burden them with how difficult it was, he would not say he felt low or depressed. He simply retired to his bedroom. It wasn't unusual for this man to sleep 10 or 11 hours each night. And since he also worked full time, you can imagine that he didn't see much of his family. But his job was so difficult, and he wanted to protect them from the effects it had on him. When his children left home, his wife found another man. He died quite young, and quite alone.

At the end of my story, the children sat quiet and wide-eyed, all of them. 'To me, your children look as if they have been scared by my story. Do you think that something similar could happen to either of you?' We all sat quietly then for a long time. I wanted my question to sink in.

We had heard of Linda's creativity in the art group she was in, how she had helped set up a women's group, and we had all seen the fine family sculpture she had just created. We all of us knew that in the past she had sacrificed her creative talents at home. I told her that before the next session she should think about how she would like to use the abilities and creative urges she had. She should not try to stop being depressed when she did this: it was no easy endeavour. She should handle any feelings that came up as she had since our first session. Thomas should not interfere or encourage her in her task. But he and the children should continue not tiptoeing around and also tell her when she looked depressed. While Linda worked at her task, Thomas should focus on time he might spend with the children, and leave Linda the opportunity to think.

In the fourth session, our last, Linda told that this past week had been worse than the one before. She said that the children made so much noise (I winked at them), and Thomas had been so critical and provocative, that she and he had had a terrible fight.

'But you were still depressed sometimes in the week.'

'Yes, of course, that's what I'm saying. But I got angry too!'

'Well . . . I thought I would talk with you this week about helping me with something. And I was a bit afraid that if you lost your depression you wouldn't be interested.' I told her I was planning to train women from the community to become group leaders for women's self-help groups. With her experience and the depth of feelings I had seen in her, I wanted her to be one of the members of the pilot group.

118

'Do you mean,' Thomas folded his arms and sat forward in his seat, 'that all these years of therapy and trips to hospital and keeping the peace were for nothing?!'

'You know, some people pretend they don't have life experiences, or they don't ever let themselves react. Linda has always admitted openly what she's felt. Now I think it's clear to all of us that the time has come when she can really help others by using her experience from all those years past.'

The experienced family therapist must be suspicious whenever a child is defined as a 'problem' (cf. Madanes 1981). It can be difficult for adults to accept differences in children, and when differences reach sufficient proportions, or are encountered by an adult with authority, a child can be referred to professionals as a problem warranting special treatment.

This is not to say that labelling or identification of problematic behaviour is always wrong. When a child is presented as a problem, some family dysfunction is being signalled. The child is the introduction to the family. The therapist must exercise diligence in assessing each case to discover where the problem lies, and for whom the problem exists.

The therapist in this case aimed to challenge the family's perception of what was problematic, and to alter the day-to-day organization within which the problematic behaviour was maintained. The children's responses revealed a pattern of control in the home. This is frequently found in homes where there is a chronic patient. The tasks strategically, and without confrontation, required new responses to Linda's way of managing her symptoms. Each family member created his own particular response, so that the home became a more wholesome, more varied environment.

The story might be subtitled 'A Case of Change Through No Change'. The strategy with Linda was to accept her symptom, and to value her statements about its effects on and in her life. I similarly accepted and valued her guilt as wife and mother, but did not suggest any resolution to her condition. Trying to cheer up, convince, or clarify the feelings of depressed persons is hopeless and tends to devalue both client and therapist. Her depression was immediately reframed as a predictable consequence of the most recent move, and of her therapy. Her emotional honesty was underlined, as was a general familial concern and sincerity, that was actually 'visible'. Furthermore, what had long been considered a disability was reclassified as a source of value to others in the community. Previous attempts to cure Linda's disability were defined as the very source of those skills through which she would communicate her knowledge and understanding to others.

The responsibility and the change which accompanied Thomas' promotion and the nature of the work itself suggested his symptom was a reality not to be neglected. The therapist's goals were for him to achieve a reasonable work-load, and to enhance the quality and quantity of his family involvement. Means to these ends included the parable of the man who died, homework which demanded that Thomas take stock of his physical condition, and the time he allowed for enjoying leisure time (mischievous) with his children.

By defining the family as a place in which it is permissible to be alone as well as with others, I introduced the possibility for a further change in behaviour, and acceptance of differences. The tasks prescribed underscored and encouraged that variability. As for the children, I merely encouraged them to be themselves, by valuing individually what each of them did well, and what they desired. The prescription to make noise (as children normally do) was to uphold their childishness so that they do not assume responsibility for their mother's chronic condition or her care.

Linda made an excellent group leader. Perhaps she spoke a bit too much at times, but that was rather a small technical point. Judith was given her pony, and there were no further reports except good ones about any of the children at school.

Note

1   For those who may not be familiar with this technique, family sculptures are a means to give a family another perspective or better understanding of itself as a system. A single family member is asked to create a 'sculpture', using family members to represent or illustrate such aspects of family systems as communication patterns, individual family roles, or family dynamics. This activity is generally followed by discussion of the representation suggested (cf. Satir 1967 and 1972).

In this case, the technique was used strategically. At the same time, it made use of the expertise Linda gained in her previous treatments, and limited her extensive descriptions of the details of her condition. Reframing the perspective of the family sculpture to what the family gained from Linda's depression, contributed to changing the way the family members saw Linda's symptom.

7 Loss

The Red Blouse

There was a snow storm the evening Elizabeth came to see me after the loss of her father. She was quite white with snow, and when I led her into the warmth of my office, the snow started melting before she could take off her overcoat. The water dripped from her coat, and her long, black hair and eyelashes. She lived a long distance from the clinic, and she had walked all the way.

'But there is no one out tonight, so I could walk undisturbed and put my thoughts into order.' she offered.

I had met Elizabeth a couple of days earlier when she visited her doctor for sleeping-pills. He suspected her sleeplessness was related to her recent bereavement. Elizabeth's father had died just a month before. That first time we met, she had Peter and Birgitte, 6 and 3 years old, with her, and we decided to meet again when she could come without the children. Up to that point, she said, she had tried to spend time as normally and agreeably as possible with her children – as she had before her father's death. Tonight, Anton was looking after them to give her the time for herself.

Once she took off her coat, Elizabeth said that she had been able to play with the children, and read to them. Yes, she had even been able to sleep since I told her it was what she had to do up until our meeting. 'But now I am afraid,' she finished, and I could see how her hands trembled as she folded them in her lap.

I asked her to tell me about her father's illness and death. In the beginning of December, following his regular annual check-up, he received the message from his hospital that there was nothing serious the matter with him. He celebrated Christmas and New Year with his three children and their families exactly as in the past. Elizabeth commented on how tired he looked, but that wasn't unusual. He tended to be affected by the cold and long darkness each winter. Shortly after the New Year, however, he was admitted to hospital, but again the report was unspecific. They said that he was sure to be quite well soon.

'How old was your father?'

'He was only 55, but he looked older. He had worked hard all his life, up to the time of his accident at work. Then he had to stop at the factory. That was two years ago.'

'What happened to him?'

'He damaged his back somehow. But I don't think he was sorry to stop working. He always wanted us to have an education. He wanted always to have one himself. So . . . '

'So his illness wasn't connected with the accident?'

There was a long silence.

'Did you visit him in hospital?'

'Yes, nearly every day. He was only there for ten days. No one told us what was wrong with him. They didn't 'phone 'til after he died that night. I drove there immediately to see him, but it was as if it wasn't him at all. All I could think about was how he looked at me when I had visited him with Anton and the children that same afternoon. When I said goodbye to him and took his hand, he looked at me. It was as if he wanted to ask something. I didn't do anything to find out what he wanted, but I still think that he wanted to say more than goodbye.

'My mother and brothers cried, but I couldn't. I couldn't cry. I haven't really cried 'til now.' And while she talked, the tears fell down on to her folded hands.

'Then you must need to cry now,' I said. 'But go on talking even if you cry.'

'I'm sure that he wanted to say something to me . . . It wasn't 'til afterwards that they told us he had cancer throughout his body . . . And I wanted so much to say goodbye to him' Her thoughts came disconnected, but they gave clear expression to what she had probably not dared to think or talk about before.

'Did you go to his funeral?' I asked.

'I went to everything, but I felt nothing doing it. It was as if I stood outside and watched it all happening. It's just now I come to think about how difficult it must have been for him. Do you think he knew?'

'Yes, I think so.'

'It was as if he wanted to say goodbye. But I still can't believe that he's not here any more. It's nearly a month ago now, but I can't stand visiting my parents' home. I can't bear to think that he won't be there. And I can't talk to Anton about it. He thought it was odd that I wanted to talk to you, but if it was necessary, of course it was OK he said . . . ' She had stopped crying. She sat silently, and thoughtfully.

'It hurts so much to lose one you really love,' I said. 'But you have to go through the mourning if you're going to be better again. Therefore it's important that you do exactly what I say. As you did the other day. Go home and find the photographs you have from your time with your father. Sit down by yourself and think through the times you've had together. Tell Anton that you have to do this if you are going to be happy again. You can cry as much as you want to. And let Anton and the children see it. It's nothing to hide. Tell them that you cry because you've lost your father. I want you to return in two days and bring with you the photo of him which you like the best.'

She brought with her a picture from her wedding. It showed the table at the reception meal. Her father sat beside her, a bit stiff in his formal wedding suit, beaming down at her.

'He looks very proud of you. Was he proud of you?'

'Yes, he always was. The way he looks here was the way he always looked at me whenever he saw me. Always as if I was something special.' She added this last bit modestly.

'Did he show it in other ways?'

'He often gave me money to buy things I wanted ... And ... once when I was a child ... he had a long time at home with my brothers and me. My mother had bad nerves and she was at the clinic. It was when I was starting school. I was afraid. We didn't talk about it. But the day before school started he bought me a red blouse. He didn't have much money — I knew even then. He'd also taken a day off from work so he could go to school with me. Besides him, there were only mothers who had brought their children for the first day. But even then he looked exactly as he does in this picture. And the red blouse was very pretty. He always wanted the best for me, only the very best.' Elizabeth's tears fell on the picture. She wiped them away carefully with the handkerchief she had brought with her.

'Was he pleased that you married?'

'Oh yes, he liked Anton so much. He liked him from the time we were engaged. But he was sorry that I was pregnant. Even if he never mentioned it, I knew he was afraid that I'd stop my kindergarten training once I had the baby. But I didn't do that. For a year and a half I left Peter at the day-care centre and made the long journey to and from teacher training school. Even if all our friends thought that — since Anton earned good money as a waiter — I should stay at home with him.'

'I do understand that he was proud of you,' I said. 'Was he as fond of Peter?'

'Yes!' she smiled. 'He always enjoyed him so much and so openly that I was nearly jealous!'

'What did he give you that you'll miss now? What more than money to buy what you wanted?'

'He gave me peace,' she said slowly, thinking while she spoke. 'It wasn't that we talked so much together when I saw him. It was enough for me just to sit quietly together with him. Perhaps he would describe a bit about what he was doing in the garden. Sometimes he asked about my work. He always thought it was exciting to hear how I managed different situations with the children. Very often, I found solutions with some problem I had in the kindergarten or at home while we talked. But it's something I really just now realize, because there were never big words between us. We always thought that my mother and my brothers talked far too much. I was more like him, so we were often just silent together. Still. But I can't get over that I didn't say goodbye to him ... '

'You'll have to do that,' I said. 'As soon as you can. You must go to his grave. You must be quite alone. Take this photo with you and then allow yourself to feel and think about whatever happens when you are there. Tell him everything, including all the things you didn't get to say before he died. And say goodbye to him.

'When can you go there?'

Four days later she came back. The weather was as the first evening, but she was different. It took me a few moments to realize what the difference was. But when she took off her duffle coat, I saw that her hands were quiet, and I could see that where her face had expressed anxiety the first evening, what shone through this evening was a fulfilment and a peace. She was still pale, with rings under her eyes. She looked like a person in sorrow, as if she had been crying very much.

She had been to the grave: 'But I didn't feel much. It was so cold. It was just so cold. Then suddenly I was angry. 'How could you do this to us!? How could you just go and let us be alone when we can't do without you?' I didn't cry. I shouted and demanded and afterwards I felt very ashamed. Because I knew he didn't do it on purpose. But it was all so cold and so empty.'

'And he will never return again.' I said.

'No, he won't come back again,' she repeated slowly. She paused, then continued, 'Then, for the first time I was able to go home to my mother. I wanted to go to her. With Anton and the children. I knew he wouldn't be there, but I managed even if we didn't talk about him. On our way home, I started crying. And then, after I had gone to bed, I cried some more. I could only think about how very cold it must be. I just wished that he could tell me how it was, that it was all right to be dead. I mean, if he could just tell me that he was all right.'

'What do you think he'd say if you could see him now?'

And she wept quietly as she answered, 'He would just be here, and then I could be happy and peaceful.'

I paused. 'But he is not here and he will never return.' She cried harder then, and at last she said, 'It's strange. Anton says I have to learn to be more open.'

'Do you want that?'

'Yes,' she said. 'Now I want to. Before I always thought the others talked much too much. But now I'm beginning to think I must express myself more.'

'Is there more you want for yourself?'

'Yes. I want to be able to take more initiative for the things we do — so that it's not always Anton who plans things and does them.'

'I'll give you a fortnight,' I said. 'During this period each day you take time to tell Anton what you have experienced that day: what you thought and felt. You also think up something all of you — or just the two of you — can do together in your spare time. If you don't feel like doing what Anton or the kids suggest then you say, "No" and don't do it. You do something you yourself want to do.

'You have to be conscious about what you do in this fortnight. It's very difficult to change a pattern you've been living with for so long, which you feel has served you well. Each time you think of your father, allow yourself to remember everything you had together with him, and allow yourself to cry over what you've lost. You can describe this to Anton too. But do remember that just as he looks at you in this picture, so it was. He wanted the very best for you. That will never change. Exactly as when he gave you the red blouse.'

A fortnight later, Elizabeth seemed to have grown at the same time younger and older. Her face was marked by grief, but it also showed a depth or life it hadn't earlier. She described how she had taken the family sledging. And how she had enjoyed herself in the snow as if she were a child again. At first her children and Anton had watched her in amazement, but as soon as they saw she really enjoyed herself, they all joined in.

And she had finally talked with her mother about her father and his death. And for the first time in her life, she said, she didn't see her mother as talking too much. 'But the best,' she said at last, 'is that Anton told me he feels safer about me and about our relationship. Even if I still stumble when I try to talk about myself or how I feel, I'm doing it. He helps me so much — he listens! I never thought he was able to do it. Perhaps . . . in a way . . . my father was in the way. As long as I had him to listen, I never needed anyone else. As long as I could go home to him, there was no need to try to talk much. And I always thought the others talked *too* much. I know that he would never have chosen to be in my way,' she said. 'And I can feel his love even now. The security he gave me I can feel. I know now I have it forever. Somehow I've seen that it is possible . . . perhaps it was necessary . . . for me to live without him.'

The findings of the Harvard Bereavement Study, a longitudinal examination of spouses' responses to sudden death, were that sudden and untimely deaths are 'potentially pathological'. Development of somatic symptoms, increased consumption of alcohol, tobacco or drugs, and persistent impaired emotional states — such as depression or anxiety — were reactions which the study identified and measured (Parkes 1981). Possible consequences of somatic or psychiatric nature are detailed in countless other studies and descriptions of grief reactions.

At the same time, Cassem redefines loss as a 'developmental showdown' at which point in his life the bereaved 'grows or else' (1975, p. 12). This view of death — for the dying patient and for his family — is substantiated in the writings and practices of Keleman (1974),

Kubler-Ross (1969), Saunders (1972) and Schneider (1981) to name but a few.

Elizabeth's father's death was not a sudden death. But because of the way in which the hospital managed both the details of his condition and the treatment he received,[1] the circumstances of his death resembled sudden death phenomenon — particularly in its effects for Elizabeth.

Traditional medical management of her somatic reaction would have been to focus on the symptoms, to subdue them and therefore to hinder her 'use' of them, or her appreciation of their significance in her overall relation to, and her dealing of, her father's death. While bereavement counselling may not be advised for all survivors, the case study illustrates the potential benefit of timely brief and intense intervention.

The intervention depicted in this case — and in the study that follows — characterizes the bereavement work at Laegernes Hus. The contact is generally brief. Elizabeth was seen four times within two weeks, with a final meeting a fortnight later. Its ultimate aims are to support the patient in establishing a realistic relationship *vis-à-vis* the deceased, and in developing new patterns of interaction which foster social continuity or growth.

A distinction of loss or bereavement work is that the therapist acknowledges and accepts the distress reactions of the patient, and does not try to alter or palliate them. Rosenblatt's historical/anthropological study of the diaries of bereaved people reveals multiformity of intensity and expression of feeling (1981). Further studies of grief reactions document:

- denial of loss
- extreme intellectualization
- acute and chronic guilt
- restlessness and increased motor activity
- tendency to irritability, hostility and outright anger
- loss of warmth in relation to others
- somatic distress

all as typical and predictable reaction modes in the face of terminal diagnosis or death of a loved one (Friedman *et al.* 1963; Janis 1958; Lindemann 1944). The work therefore demands understanding and acknowledgement of the variety of reaction responses to loss, and recognition that they tend to be transitional phenomena. In starting 'where the patient is', the therapist identifies and regards the patient's reaction response as the 'normal' or appropriate one for the individual concerned at the particular moment.

According to Lindemann, one of the biggest problems in acute grief work appears to be that patients often try to avoid the intense distress connected with the grief experience, and to avoid the expression of emotion which accompanies it (1944). Therefore what is construed as problem-creating behaviour is the patient's perception or management of these reactions, rather than the reactions themselves. It is not unusual, for example, for grieving patients to interpret their 'loss of warmth' in the face of obvious need of contact with others as an indicator of mental disturbance in themselves. Medical personnel tend to contribute to this problem-creating potential by prescribing medication which dampens or alleviates the reaction, thereby reinforcing the notion that these reactions are dangerous or wrong — something to be remedied (Weiner 1975).

The guide-lines for working with patients in grief suggested by Lindemann have been applied and expanded for the patient contact at Laegernes Hus (ibid.):

- accepting the pain of bereavement
- reviewing the patient's relationship with the deceased
- becoming acquainted with the patient's mode of reaction
- accepting expression of sorrow and sense of loss
- working through fears of insanity or surprising change in emotion
- accepting verbalization of guilt
- finding an acceptable formulation of relationship to the deceased
- discovering or developing personal resources in the patient's social network
- establishing new patterns of behaviour.

Re-grief therapy is a model of intensive, short-term psychotherapy developed at the University of Virginia for treatment of 'established pathological mourners'. Established pathological grief is regarded as a clinical entity in its own right. It is a category comprising patients who are fixated in the initial reactions to death (shock, numbness, disbelief and hope that the deceased will return) long after the death itself. Volkan describes these patients as caught in the struggle of loss and restitution, without coming to resolution. The model aims to bring into the patient's consciousness memories of the deceased and of experiences had together, in order to test these against reality in order for the patient to accept the sorrow, guilt, anger, relief over what has happened. Patients are encouraged to understand, or come to terms with, their responses to the death so that they are able to free themselves from excessive bondage to the dead (Manocchio 1981; Volkan 1975, pp. 334–5).[2]

The aims of grief work at Laegernes Hus resemble those of re-grief therapy, namely for the patient to establish a realistic relationship *vis-à-vis* the deceased, and develop new patterns of interaction which foster social continuity and growth.

The elements of intervention which characterize re-grief therapy are

'Demarcation' Phase   This is important from the start of therapy, since the pathological mourner is in a chronic state of hope of reunion with the dead. The patient is encouraged to make rational distinctions between what belongs to himself and what belongs to the one he has lost. Detailed history is taken in non-directive dialogue. The reader will have noted that in this case and the next the verbal responses of the therapist are short, simple and accepting.

The taking of a history initiates a process whereby the patient begins distinguishing boundaries between himself and his representation of the deceased. He is encouraged to evaluate aspects of his relationship with the deceased: what was difficult, enjoyable, special, important. The therapist listens to his story to understand better in which ways the deceased was significant. It is important for the therapist to be able to comprehend the nature of the dependency that prevents the patient from letting go or allowing that the deceased is dead. Circumstances around the death should be described in detail, as part of the patient's story: how the deceased died, family circumstances, medical management, what care was administered or regretted by the patient. This should include whatever elements the patient considers relevant to the story.

'Linking Objects'   These are identified by the patient as special tokens or representations of the dead person. Linking objects are brought to the session and the patient is encouraged to look at, touch and discuss them: why are they important; what place did they have for the deceased; what meaning they have now for the patient. The patient is encouraged to discuss what was learned from or shared with the deceased.

More actively, the therapist helps the patient to *review the circumstances of the death*: specifically how it happened, how the patient received news of it, family reactions, details of the funeral and internment. The patient is encouraged to evaluate these events and his or her part in them in order to awaken the patient's understanding and to discover unfinished business. In this phase the therapist helps explain and interpret the relationship between the patient and the deceased, so that the patient can better understand their feelings.

The therapist underlines the reality of the death. He does this either by asking the patient when he realized the deceased was no longer alive, or by reiterating that the deceased will not return. Volkan describes a tendency in his patients' experience for some mishap around the funeral. But as Elizabeth's story shows, hospital management of the final stages of life can contribute to pathological mourning. The final stage of treatment is reached, says Volkan, 'when the patient sees that he wanted something from the dead, or that the dead represented part of himself' (p. 339). This conclusion is embodied in Elizabeth's altered responses and attitudes to her father and her spouse. The patient at this point shifted her demands to the network in which she lived, away from her preoccupation with the deceased.

When compared with the story, it can be seen that Volkan's phases do not necessarily occur in chronological order. It can further be said that they may overlap within the course of treatment. Volkan generally distinguishes photographs from other linking objects, while at Laegernes Hus, photos are as likely to be used as any other object of the deceased's as the basis of therapeutic discussion.

The story also demonstrates how the therapist can formulate a projection of positive intent on the part of the deceased. Loving and hope-filled sentiments of the deceased are defined by the therapist as continuing support and encouragement for the growth and development of the living. Elizabeth was assured that what she 'had gained' from her father was not lost at his death. He would always want the best for her and be behind her in all her ventures.

This positive use of remembering the deceased — as a base for the development of the patient's social and psychological breadth — can be seen in another form in the next story, that of Elenor.

I'm Not Hungry, Grandma

One of the doctors asked me late one afternoon to telephone and make an appointment with one of our older patients. She had visited him to discuss her grandchild Elenor. The doctor recommended that both she and her husband come with the girl. He promised I would ring her for an appointment.

Over the telephone Berthe asked if it was really necessary that her husband join her, and I explained that it was important for me to get to know all three of them. She agreed to try to persuade her husband to join her, but that they couldn't bring the girl. That would be impossible.

I was five minutes late the morning they came. Irving made a note of this by looking at his watch as he sat on the chair which I offered. He was tall, pleasantly slim, and had thick white hair. Even though it was only the beginning of May, he was already sunburnt. Beneath his thick coal-black eyebrows, his eyes were dark blue and intensely alert.

Berthe was the first to enter my office, and did so in a way that she both entered and apologized for doing so at the same time. Her whole manner in fact was apologetic. She was a little pale, and though well dressed, she emanated a touch of servitude. Her hair was coloured artificially, but once it had been strawberry blonde. It was clear that having it well groomed and coloured was her norm. Her tweed suit was expensive but a bit too big for her. At points during the conversation she shifted in her seat to hitch up the skirt — a move which was not as discreet as she would have wished. Her hands were little and elegant, tipped with pale-pink nail polish and clutching a pair of beige kid gloves that she wrung as she sat in my office. The two adults made a pair in that both sat slightly hunched over, heads tilted forward. The difference between them was that Irving hunched over because of his hearing, to get his ear closer to the speaker. Berthe leaned over anxiously in order to be able to attend any question, to show her willingness to contribute. I judged them to be in their early sixties. It turned out that Irving was 68 and Berthe 62 years of age. I apologized for being late.

Berthe replied that it could easily happen. Irving merely raised those coal-black eyebrows in response, and sat even more upright in his chair. It was clear that he felt it was already time to leave. I thanked him for joining us. His hint of a smile suggested he now felt I was trying to take away his weapons. He said that the thing with Elenor was his wife's business. Those matters were always her business.

'You live far away from here?' I said.[3]

'We don't change doctors as we change clothes,' Irving answered. 'In all the years we lived in this district we have used the doctors here, and we haven't moved so far away that we can't continue to come to Laegernes Hus.'

Berthe explained then that her husband was a retired officer. On retirement, they had chosen to move to a bigger town, for social reasons. Both of them wanted to join a bridge club. He wanted to play golf more regularly. She had hoped to take part in some volunteer welfare work, but . . .

And as she paused, I said, 'But something prevented you from doing it.'

The retired officer sat silent. Looking straight before him, he perhaps did not see that his wife appealingly sought his eyes. His hands gripped the arms of his chair. Berthe shifted the gloves from one hand to the other and continued. 'Shortly after we moved, our only daughter — and only child — became ill. It was discovered that she had a cancer of the liver, and in two months she died. She'd never been sick before, so it was impossible to comprehend . . . Of course it was worse for my son-in-law and the children.' As she spoke she unwound and her voice became more steady. Irving covertly wiped a tear from his eye.

'And one of those children was Elenor,' I said.

'Yes, Elenor was 12 years old when Bente died,' said Berthe. 'And her little brother Alex was only 7.'

'How did Elenor come to you?'

Without recrimination, Berthe described how Elenor had strived to replace her mother. She learned to cook and bake, and took responsibility for reading and helping little Alex with his school work. In less than a year her father had remarried. It was soon clear that Elenor would have difficulties accepting a new mother. 'It was never open battle, but when they learned a baby was expected, one day Elenor just disappeared. She was found the next day on her mother's grave.'

'Are all these details necessary?' Irving looked indisposed. Berthe glanced uncertainly at me.

'Yes, I want to know everything.'

Berthe continued, 'She refused to go home again, and who could help her better than us?'

'So your life was suddenly changed from the one you had been looking forward to. It must have been a very difficult decision for you to make.'

'It was our simple duty,' replied Irving, as if there were nothing more to say to that. But he cleared his throat and his eyes were glistening.

'She's been with us for a year and a half,' said Berthe. 'It's really gone much better than I dared to hope. Occasionally she goes home for a weekend, even though it is still difficult for her. So that shouldn't be the reason for her being so unhappy and unwilling to go to school now. And she doesn't want to eat properly. And often I can see she has been crying, even though she tries to hide it.'

'What does she say when you ask her?'

'That she has a headache. And that she cannot get along with her schoolmates. I didn't take it so seriously until her doctor — she has her own doctor where we live — told me that she needed psychiatric help.'

'How did he come to say that? Was it when she didn't want to go to school?'

'Well, yes. But I think that it had more to do with my telling him that one day when Elenor had gone out, I found her mother's photograph lying crumpled into a little ball beneath her bed . . . We simply cannot understand it, but . . . ' Berthe glanced over at her husband who still sat stiffly without moving body or eyes. 'She was so close to her mother. They had so much together. Elenor has also stopped playing the piano now. The two of us had started playing duets. It's taken me some time to remember how to play,' she added. 'But it was one of the things I used to do with Bente, and I knew that she and Elenor had started playing together.' Now she was wiping away her tears.

'What do you think about Elenor and the way she is behaving now?' I turned directly to Irving.

He looked full at me and his critical response seemed in contradiction to what his eyes expressed: 'I've never occupied myself with children,' were his words. 'As I said earlier, this is my wife's area.'

'I see. But you agreed it was the right thing to ask me for help,' I stated. He only nodded solemnly. It was clear that he wouldn't say more. I told Berthe that there was nothing psychiatrically the matter in a daughter being angry at her mother — even if she were dead. Elenor had some difficulties just now which she wanted to talk about.

'Obviously she cannot cry out loud, or grieve, or even weep without your hearing her. And I'm sure she doesn't want to frighten or trouble you more than you are, so she can't express or get rid of her anger in any other way than crumpling the picture. It's the thing that most represents her dead mother.'

Berthe sat still for a long time. At last she said, 'Perhaps it's not as unnatural as we thought. We have never forgiven our son-in-law for being angry at Bente when she was ill and dying. But perhaps Bente also felt that she deserted or failed him in leaving them all.'

Her husband was still silent. There was movement in his face both around the mouth and eyes, but it was impossible to read. I said nothing when Berthe asked him 'Or what do you think, Father?' She seemed satisfied with the way he cleared his throat. Or perhaps he moved in some way which conveyed something to her. I couldn't see it . . . .

'The doctor said that you could help us,' Berthe said finally.

'I want to talk with Elenor,' I answered. 'When can she come?'

I saw Elenor only once. She was of average height, with a fair complexion and big blue eyes, and with curly chestnut hair. Her hands and feet were remarkably small, and she was very slim without looking skinny or unhealthy. When I considered how her grandparents looked I could imagine how much she must look like her own mother. Berthe brought her, but insisted on our talking alone together. When she left the room, I asked Elenor if that was the way she wanted it and she answered, 'Yes, it's already so difficult for her.'

Elenor told me how she had liked moving to her grandparents' home. And how at the same time she became best friends with Toni, the most popular girl in her class. 'I never really had a best friend before,' she said. 'When I was younger I guess I never thought of it, and after Mother died, I had no time for friends. My brother and father also missed her so much.

'I don't know if I did something wrong, but then suddenly everything at school changed. It was as if they had all started plotting against me. All the others in the class and Toni too. Sometimes they laugh at my clothes. They think I'm old-fashioned. Especially after a party — you see Grandma always thinks you have to be neat and proper when you go to a party. And I'm not always allowed to do the same as everybody else. Grandma is from another generation, you see.'

'Then you have no friends at all now?' I asked Elenor. She did have one friend, but he was in another class, so most of the time she felt very alone. And she wanted a girl-friend . . . and anyway she wouldn't let Toni decide how it would be for her. And nor would she hurt her Grandma who wanted so much to do the best for her.

Elenor described Toni at length, and very imaginatively. I could see the tall, slim, light 14-year-old friend, the comfortable home, five brothers and sisters, two of whom had started at university, and two at the gymnasium. It was obvious that Toni's success meant healthy competition for Elenor, not only in regard to social ken, but also in everyday matters: clothes, sports, music and friends.

'What are you doing in your spring break?' I asked Elenor. 'It starts in three days.'

'Grandpa promised us a trip to Copenhagen,' she said. They were going to a concert and also to the ballet.

'Well, then, I don't want you to go to school before the break. But I want you to start back again at school after the break, when you are fresh and in form from your good time in Copenhagen. The first thing you do is to go to Toni and say something that you think is nice about the way she looks. The way you describe her it sounds very easy to do that. Perhaps she's wearing something nice, or her hair that day is especially lovely. But whatever you find, start the day by telling her of something that you like about her. When she does something clever during the class — and it sounds as if she does rather often — then look at her and give her a smile to show you can see what she's done well. And in the break between lessons walk over to her and tell her exactly what she did well in the class, what you valued. Now don't overdo it — you know what I mean — don't cling to her. But be very honest in your appreciation and the feelings you show her.'

Elenor looked at me. 'Do you really think it will help?'

'I know it,' I said.

Then she told me of her grandmother's worries about her appetite. I told her, 'I'll take care of that with grandma, but only on one condition. You must talk to your grandmother about your mother. Ask her about all the things you want to know about her. And all the things you would have asked your mother if she were still alive.'

'I can't do that! It's too much to ask of Grandma!' Elenor cried. 'She also misses Mother. If I ask about her, I'll remind her of her sadness.'

'Do you really think she can look at you every day without being reminded of her daughter?' I asked. Elenor didn't reply, but it was clear she was thinking about what we had discussed.

'So is this an agreement?' I asked. And she nodded. And for the first time there were tears in her eyes. 'Telephone me a week after school has started again. And tell me how it goes,' I instructed her. 'And now we'll go out and I'll get hold of Grandma.'

While we had been talking, Berthe wandered restlessly about the corridors of the clinic. When she joined us, she was still nervous and agitated. When she spoke her words came out harshly and over-loud, as they do when people try to mask their worry. 'Well, have you two had a nice talk together?'

I took Berthe's hand and led her into my office. I told her that Elenor and I had talked about how many things she, Berthe, would be able to tell Elenor about the times when her mother was 15 years old.

About all the tricks she had played and about the things the two of them did together when they enjoyed themselves. 'I'm sure you have many old pictures from that time that you and Elenor can look over together.

'But Elenor must take care of her own eating and school problems. She's old enough for that.'

'That will be difficult,' said Berthe. 'She must be hungry when she comes home from school and won't eat anything.'

'I know it will be difficult,' I said, 'but that will be much easier than letting Elenor manage her own troubles at school. You have to work on your own memories and tell Elenor about all the problems you had with her mother at school, when she was 15.

'Will you do that?'

'I'll try,' she promised.

When Elenor telephoned me she had no more problems with her schoolmates. 'But it's still hard for Grandma not to feed me.' Her gently ironic tone confirmed my first impression of her humour and maturity.

'And how about talking about Mother?' I asked.

'It's getting better and better,' she said and her voice sounded as fresh and hopeful as a 15 year old's can.

I have not heard from Elenor since then, but three weeks later there was a bouquet of pink roses on my desk when I came in to work. Attached was Irving's card.

'The Red Blouse' demonstrates the use of a model which confronts grief directly. Re-grief therapy is primarily an individual contact which seeks (1) to alter the patient's perception of, and relation, to the deceased, and (2) to maintain or extend the social contacts within the patient's social network, in order to prevent or offset isolation and its potential attending consequences: loneliness, depression, and so on.

'I'm Not Hungry, Grandma' illustrates an application of brief problem-focused therapy. Intervention here shifted the family's perception of the problem, and the family structure. The story exemplifies a fundamental precept of brief therapy, that short term, problem-focused intervention can elicit benefits beyond the boundaries of the problem specifically defined. Constructive ramifications evolve once the 'vicious cycle' of behaviour which creates or maintains the problem state is redirected (Haley 1976 and Weakland et al. 1974).

The professional works in this situation as an identifier of needs and mobilizer of resources (Lyall and Vachon 1975, p. 227). Identification of needs in this case comes through the formulation of the problem by the grandparents, their medical advisor and Elenor. The story demonstrates the importance of discovering for whom the problem exists as a problem, and in which ways the circumstances are problematic. Elenor's elaboration of her view of the situation, of her social circle at school, and of her concerns for her grandmother were vital to fill out the initial presentation of her problem as provided by her grandparents.

A number of therapeutic 'themes' or issues came out of this problem formulation. School attendance, meal consumption, painful memories, concern for the grief of others, participation in her peer network were all aspects of Elenor's teenage predicament. When a family problem is defined around a young person, a primary goal of the therapist is to avoid prolongation of the child's difficulty by formalizing, professionalizing, or crystallizing isolated elements of the young person's behaviour. This begins to happen as soon as behaviour or symptoms are regarded as pathological or suitable for treatment (Haley 1976 and 1980).

With the aims of assisting Elenor through a classically difficult period, and to avoid crystallizing her 'problems', the therapist, from the very start, reframed and confirmed Elenor's 'worrisome' behaviour as normal and predictable grief reactions. At the same time, Berthe and Irving were supported and upheld in the job they had done with Elenor. This support of parental figures is important for a number of reasons. By acknowledging the hard work, responsibilities, worries, and accomplishments of this role, the therapist can reframe the parents' (or grandparents') concerns as normal and healthy, and thereby avert exacerbation of the problem by their panicking, over-reacting, or calling in further professional assistance. The therapist also seeks to emphasize the differences between the generations, and to encourage adult respect for the young person's changing needs. Elenor was no longer a child, but a mature teenager capable of articulating her thoughts and feelings, and of starting to take responsibility for her actions. A second purpose in encouraging Berthe and Elenor to discuss Elenor's mother was to foster improved interaction between them.

The aims of treatment for Elenor were to support her perceptions of the circumstances. The therapist sought to open acceptable outlets for discussions about her mother and her family, and for the expression of her grief. By discussing her school situation, the therapist reinforced Elenor's trust in her own perceptions and abilities to set personal goals and to influence their outcome in her social circle.

The initial assessment of young persons met in therapy is mediated by a number of factors. The experience of the therapist is the key. How much she has learned from work with young persons and learned *from* young persons will be directly reflected in expectations of sensitivity, sensibility and normal behaviour in youth.

The avoidance of prolonged treatment or institutionalization for young persons is an explicit objective of psychosocial intervention at Laegernes Hus. Moreover, the notion of historical family development or reconstruction (Satir 1967) which allows that the 'world view' of parents (and grandparents) is different from that of the offspring is useful in the assessment of situations such as Elenor's. The differences between how people of different ages view the world influence adults' perceptions of a child's behaviour, so that what is different seems troubling, worrying, or dangerous. This phenomenon is a significant one as the therapist formulates the problem and seeks to discover problem-creating or -maintaining elements. It is important that the therapist stresses these differences, as well as the differences between the roles and responsibilities of the different generations. Adult matters are not the responsibility of children, who are encouraged to develop relationships appropriate to their sibling and peer networks (Minuchin 1978 and 1981).

In the meeting with Elenor the therapist assessed how the girl presented herself in terms of appearance, her openness and style of response to questions, and as a representative of her age group within the family life-cycle (that is, as a teenager). As the young person responds to questioning, the therapist takes note of the world picture he or she presents. Is it realistic, appropriate for her age level? Does it reflect an awareness of self and of other persons and factors in the environment? Since the perceptions of the involved adults (those generally presenting the problem) are very likely to differ from those of the child or teenager and, since the young person is most often the eventual target of whatever treatment or help is sought, it is most important to weigh these factors seriously. In Alan's story, in contrast to Elenor's, the therapist's evaluation of Alan's presentation of self, his history of manipulation of adults, the structural weaknesses within his family, and the crisis-precipitating act he committed prompted the therapist to involve him in intensive treatment, with contact over a considerably longer period.

The therapist attempts to reframe signs and actions positively from the start of contact, and throughout, at the same time taking seriously the circumstances defined by the family. But it must be admitted that it is not always useful — or possible — to do so. The next case study, which examines another kind of loss, shows the sort of difficulties this can present.

Closed Doors: An Example of Unsuccessful Therapy

> All happy families are alike but an unhappy family is unhappy after its own fashion.

This maxim opens one of the greatest depictions of the passion and pain of family drama ever written — Tolstoy's *Anna Karenina* (1971, p. 13). The couple who sat opposite me this early spring day had, too, a style of their own.

Dorothy, 42, was fair and blonde. Her clothes were expensive, but if you did not think about it, you would not recognize how well they looked. She is always dressed in grey in my memory. Philip was tall. His face was very pale. What was left of his hair was nearly black. For a man of 48, he was in remarkably fine form. Dorothy, on the other hand, was extremely thin.

They were referred to me on the basis of Dorothy's medical history. For the past two years she had suffered a variety of somatic complaints: headaches, backaches, and most recently a lump in her right breast. She was scheduled for an operation. Her doctor had already stated the lump was not malignant, but she nevertheless expressed the belief that the couple would benefit from talking with me at this time.

Their sexual life was their biggest problem, they agreed at our first meeting. Since they had their last child, a girl of 11, the couple had intercourse twice a month on average, and then only just before Dorothy's period. The rest of the time, as they described it, Dorothy was too tight. Over the past nine years they had consulted innumerable doctors and had received more advice than they could remember. Gradually, they came to accept that the doctor who said they could expect to wait 15 years before their sex life would be normal again probably knew best.

Both were cross and dissatisfied. They complained of their new home town. Two years previously, Philip had been promoted to Personnel Chief for the department of his firm. The promotion required a move. Their old home town had been ideal, according to Dorothy. She loved the town itself. Its social life was incomparable, and its schools outstanding. It had taken more than a year for their four children to get used to the new schools, and still they were not happy or settled. Dorothy was a qualified primary school teacher and had been working where they lived before. She was unable to get an appointment in the new town, although she was offered supply teaching occasionally. 'It would never be satisfying after having been used to my own class, own plan and real colleagues,' she said. Philip was happy with his new job because he loved working with people, but he claimed genuine worry over Dorothy's situation. He expressed understanding at the difficulties she must be experiencing when no one was able to make use of her capabilities. She was normally the one everyone sought for advice when they had difficulties. He stated very clearly that he wanted to work on their sexual problem. They had attempted many treatments and solutions over the years. He was willing to do anything I suggested. Both assured me that they wanted to stay together. Neither of them wanted a divorce.

Philip believed that they could get something out of their life together. Dorothy said that since nobody or nothing had been able to help up to now, she doubted whether I could help them. But she guessed that 'Nothing worse could happen by coming.'

I said that if I were to help them I wanted to see them with their children. They brought their children three times. By the start of the second session, it was clear that Philip held the role of a strong, authoritarian patriarch. He reacted to his children with loud, angry exclamations. At times his face became white and his voice so high and tight that it cracked. He banged the arms of his chair or shook his fists threateningly. This occurred several times, particularly when the children sniggered or teased each other about what was going on in the session. Dorothy interrupted Philip often, defending the children and blaming him for such behaviour. Her accusations artfully revealed his inadequacies at home and she managed to imply that she took care of everything alone. As far as I can remember I did not get to ask her one single question in the first half-hour of this session with the children. She accompanied her commentary with appealing eye contact to me. Despite his shouting at the children, it seemed impossible for Philip to respond to any of her accusations.

To say that this session was different from our first meeting would not merely be a gross simplification, but an acute depreciation of the chaos, drama and constant din which filled my office that day. It persisted to the moment when the family realized that tears were running down little Sophie's cheeks. Then they stopped speaking, one by one. I asked Sophie if she would tell me why she was crying. Sobbing and stuttering, she said that her father thought she was dumb. Everything she did was wrong at school and at home. I looked around the family circle to discover Ian, 15, gripping the arms of his chair so tightly that his knuckles were white. His face was flushed as red as a beet, and he was on the verge of crying when he blurted out, 'I'm so afraid they'll get divorced!'

Again, the expression on each face changed. The two older brothers — Brian, 18, and Steve, 17 — nudged each other and shook their heads without looking at Ian. Little Sophie had stopped crying. She sat with her mouth open, and she peered at her mother. Dorothy shifted uneasily in her chair. She glanced out of the corner of her eye at her husband. It was Philip who finally broke the silence, brusquely: 'Nonsense. That's just something you made up.'

Dorothy had pulled herself together: 'Several of his schoolmates,' she confided to me, 'have divorced parents, or they have moved from one to another in the past.'

'Have your mother and father told you why they brought you here today?' I asked Ian. He shook his head, and when I looked enquiringly at the other children, Steven said that their father just told them they had to come. Now I asked Philip to tell his children the reason. He shifted himself in his chair and cleared his throat a couple of times. Then he said,

'Well. Look. Mother and I tend to think that there was something that should be changed. You also know that Mother has been very ill over the past years and . . . '

Here Dorothy interrupted him. For the first time he looked relieved when it happened. 'Yes, and the doctor said that it might help – which I also told you.'

All four children looked puzzled. I asked Brian if he understood the reason now. He nodded. But when I asked him to explain it to Sophie, his face immediately assumed the same supercilious look as earlier. He told me I could do it myself. The idea was mine. Again Philip was furious. He shouted at him and called him an impudent cad, and ordered him to behave. Dorothy followed the cue and in her indirect way indicated she thought he was a bad example for them, being so explosive. He ought to give his children reasons instead of orders. All this, and at the same time giving me appealing glances.

Philip declared with an ingratiating smile that it must be clear that they had communication difficulties. What he really wanted was some organized plan for the jobs at home. So that Dorothy would be less tired in the evenings – so she could be free of housework in the evenings.

I asked Dorothy what would happen if she stopped cleaning up after everybody. She answered that there would be sports clothes, school papers and books all over the house. It would be unbearable. Nor would there be any clean clothes, because it was she who sorted everything for washing, just as she cleaned all their rooms. As the time had run out, I gave her the task of writing down what jobs the children could do for themselves. And instructed her not to complain or say anything about this until our next meeting.

Philip was given the task of noting wherever he saw a possibility for some change in the household management. Nor was he to discuss his findings until we saw one another again. Ian was to make a budget to show how much pocket money he realistically needed, since, during the session, his main complaint was that he did not receive enough. And Sophie, as she had expressed a hope that the family could do more things together as a family, should record all her ideas about things she would like to do with the rest of the family. I asked the elder brothers if they would return next time. It was possible that if they came they might be able to assist me in my work with the family. All agreed to do their tasks.

At the next session, I video-taped them as they related to one another the outcome of their tasks. Having listened to her tell it in person, we watched Dorothy explain how she had given up after the first day when she realized that every day the entries would be the same. That very day Philip had forgotten a note she had given him about what he was to buy in town. And of course he came home with the wrong things.

Philip had drafted a housework rota which involved everyone. Only Sophie was willing even to contemplate what he suggested. The elder brothers said there was no time possible for these things. Dorothy added that it was unlikely that even Philip would do the chores he had designated for himself. Ian's budget made his big brothers laugh loudly. It was detailed and exact. Dorothy interjected that Ian knew that she would never say no if he really needed more money, while in the same moment Philip cried out at the amount Ian had allotted for records. He told how as a boy he had to earn his own money for entertainment. Sophie had found three things she wanted them to do in common: watch certain TV programmes, have a picnic and have a nice dinner.

At this point, I was innocent enough to hope there was a chance of this family agreeing on something. All said they could imagine eating a nice dinner together (in retrospect they must have had more imagination than I: I still cannot imagine such an event ever taking place amongst them). I gave them the task in the next 15 minutes to devise a dinner menu, a time and venue, and decide how to share the preparation of it. Each topic or suggestion seemed to self-destruct in moments. Each one of them demonstrated their own personal style of creating obstacles or dashing suggestions. As we watched the video-tape of this task afterwards, Philip remarked that it very much resembled the few meals they ate together at home. Sophie was disappointed to see that it would probably be impossible for them to do anything together ever.

'If this family has anything in agreement, it's that you all have a very acutely developed critical sense.' Actually, I only wanted to see them leave my office, but I gave them paper and pens. I asked each one to draw a picture of himself and at least one other family member, and to write down three things he liked about that person, and one thing that could be different. All sat surprisingly still and drew. When the time was up, no one had finished: they were having difficulties in finding things to write to go with the pictures. The two-hour session was at its end, so their task until the next session, I told them, was to finish the drawings. They could add others if they liked, but they should not look at each other's drawings until we saw one another once again.

Nevertheless, Brian and Steve ended up combining their drawings. Brian had drawn Sophie, Steve and Dorothy, and Steve added Philip and Ian at the edge of Brian's paper. The drawings were funny and rather good. In response to the second part of the task, they covered the rest of the paper with graffiti: 'dumb', 'crazy', 'retarded', 'cheap'. Sophie drew everyone, and so had her father. Philip had no difficulties in finding admirable qualities in his wife, as well as the four children he criticized so volubly. The family sat quite still when he read these off. 'I think I am the one most astonished,' he said. 'But this has really been a useful experience for me.'

Dorothy looked put out when Philip teased her about not being allowed to see her pictures. She retorted with the familiar response that she did not have the time to devote to such things because everybody demanded so much of her. 'Besides that,' she finished, 'we weren't supposed to show the drawings before now.' She had drawn Ian. The drawing of herself she would not show. She had not been able to find three things she liked about herself. I could see that she was glad, though, when Ian had made his drawing of her. And while she did not comment, she smiled to herself when Ian, Sophie and Philip read out what they liked about her.

'I can see how much I have to change now,' Philip declared towards the end of the session. When Dorothy said to no one in particular that good intentions were not enough, he asked her if she would help him. 'You just have to tell me when I relapse,' he said.

Dorothy said she needed to see an honest effort before she would do anything. He quickly replied that this would be easier in the coming week, since she would be in hospital for the breast surgery. I asked how the family would manage without her. Dorothy answered that she expected the house to look like a tip when she returned. They had enough clean clothes. At least that wouldn't be a problem while she was away. Sophie, Ian and Philip all expressed the hope and their intentions that she would come home to a clean and tidy house.

I asked Dorothy if she was afraid that her lump was malignant. She said that she absolutely believed the doctor's word that it was not. Of course she had moments of worry and she would be relieved after the operation, to know its outcome for sure. But she preferred not to talk about it at home or here. Such discussion made children uneasy and it was always too early to do that. Philip confirmed their shared belief that children should be as untroubled as possible. You are only a child once. What's more, they had their own problems in missing their old friends and trouble finding new ones in the town.

I thanked Brian and Steve for participating and said that if they ever thought they might want help, they could contact me.

A fortnight later the couple returned alone. Dorothy explained that Ian and Sophie thought they didn't gain that much from coming, and she agreed they could remain at home. Philip noted his dissension, but expressed his reluctance to impose his will on his children. He had seen that in the long run they would not gain from his doing that.

Dorothy held her hand to her breast. I could see in the way she sat that it still hurt her. To my enquiry she answered that the operation had gone well and the lump had been found benign. She was not finding it easy to keep quiet as the doctor had directed her, returning to such a household as hers. Philip smiled good-naturedly. He said they had all really been very busy. He wanted to help her but it was not one of her strong points to keep still. Plus, it was hard to do things well enough to satisfy her. Dorothy grimaced. She closed her eyes and her face briefly stiffened with pain. Then she sighed and said in a very tired voice that there were limits to what one could stand of disorder and filth. Besides that, she had had to help Sophie catch up with the homework she had missed while Dorothy was in hospital.

Philip had on the whole been much more relaxed and less explosive, but at her statement, his face turned white with anger: 'I thought we explicitly agreed that I shouldn't have to hear these kinds of things any more. That all of you would help me to see when I said or did anything which made Sophie feel dumb. I'm really trying to pay attention, to say exactly what I mean, and nearly all the time I'm aware of how much you mean to me, all of you! I'm trying to change my way of being with you. I get so angry when you talk as if everything were still the same!'

'Is this supposed to be different?' She smiled and at once her face was indulgent and contemptuous. She crossed her legs at the knee and bobbed her foot up and down in my direction. 'Has anything at all perhaps happened to change what we originally came here for?'

'I feel that much has happened,' Philip said emotionally. 'Now we can talk together. And I can see how much I have let you down. I'm willing to accept that it will take time before you can believe I'll be different in the future. But I must know for sure that you'll tell me what you want of me, and when you think I'm doing something wrong or falling back into my old patterns.'

She shrugged. I asked her what she thought. She answered dramatically that she was in doubt of many things. She wondered if there was any point in coming to talk with me. She believed the children were right. They knew how to behave towards one another without any outside help. Philip stared at her and asked why she agreed the night before that it was necessary for the two of them to come today.

'*You* thought it was so excellent!' she shouted at him. 'And I always do what *you* think we should do. Do you think that I am really interested in running after athletes or folk-singers because *you* want to keep up your interests? I get exercise enough when I run around tidying up after you!'

The wonder in Philip's face turned to anger. But he controlled himself and said softly 'Isn't there anything at all you want from me?' And after the long silent pause, he asked 'But do you want us to go on living together?'

'What options have I got with four kids?' she spat at him. 'If it hadn't been for them, we'd have been divorced many years ago.'

Philip looked towards me without seeing anything. He said he was shocked. They had never touched on the subject of divorce, always agreed that you stick together when you bring children into the world. He loved Dorothy just as he did when they met 20 years ago, and he was unable to believe that she was serious in what she said.

'*You* are not the one who has given up everything time after time. *You* insisted that I give birth to Sophie even if I could have had an abortion at that time. *You* wanted that job and it meant that I had to once more give up my own work, and move to this godless place . . . ' she stopped only to catch her breath, but Philip said calmly, 'We've been through all this many times. Both before and since we moved. And we know that it's not to be changed now. What we can change is our future. And you're not so old that it's too late to get further training. Your brain is good. You're no dummy. And I'm willing to help you in all the ways I can while you're doing it.' His face changed as he spoke, so that by the end of his speech it matched his rousing message. But Dorothy doubted that things could be different from before. She had been disappointed so often when he had promised something that she now preferred to trust only herself. Belief in self was all she had left.

Philip shook his head with irritation. 'That just shows how much we have to work on. We have to go on trusting one another. It's a question of rebuilding that trust.' He wanted me to help them clarify their future. There was no shortage of willingness from him. Dorothy did not think however that they could gain from more therapy. But if Philip wanted, so of course she would attend.

I told them I was willing to work with one of them or both together if they both wanted it. But they should consider more closely the things they had discussed in my office and not make a decision yet. They should just know that all the possibilities were not yet closed.

'Life Transition', 'Crisis', 'Responsibility', 'Using Experience', 'Loss'. The chapter titles are not all terms of the same order. Life transition, crisis and loss indicate life events or sets of circumstances which occasion possibilities — probabilities — of qualitative alterations in the lives of the persons involved: enlightenment, disaster, development, physical disease, and so on (Schneider 1981, among many others). Using experience and responsibility, connote personal qualities which bring to bear the individual's response to life events: how he or she manages or 'uses' them.

The five titles do not exhaustively represent categories of life events or personal qualities. Nor do they signify orthodox diagnostic categories in any medical, psychiatric or behavioural science. As chapter titles they purposefully direct attention beyond the conventional divisions.

These two classes — life events and personal qualities — in fact echo the categories used in ecological studies of how health is influenced by the individual's relation to his social environment. Early enquiries in this investigation concentrated on the nature of specific stressful or problematic situations, and the personality factors which appeared to differentiate individuals' success in managing and adapting to environmental conditions (Dohrenwend and Dohrenwend 1978; Gottlieb 1981; Hinkle and Wolff 1958; Holmes and Rahe 1967).

If the psychosocial practitioner accepts that 'psychological characteristics' are significant in helping the individual cope with the effects of life experiences (Hinkle 1974), and that the social network or environment contain both problem-generating factors and the means for individuals to survive (Eckenrode and Gore 1981; Gottlieb 1981; Maddison and Raphael 1972), then intervention can be conceived of as preventative by

1   encouraging and supporting the patients' personal or psychological qualities which are believed to help individuals through periods of stress, crisis or challenge — for example, responsibility, learning from and using experiences, self identity/self-esteem, ability to express wants and needs, ability to achieve goals, ability to anticipate events (Eckenrode and Gore, ibid., Gottlieb, ibid., Hinkle, ibid., Pegg and Pegg 1975, among others).

2   encouraging and building on the patients' social resources (persons, agencies, and so on) and their ability to draw on these resources (behaviour). In qualitative analyses of significant others, it is family, friends, neighbours and kin who generally feature as most valuable resources in times of need or crisis (Bloom 1979; Caplan 1974; Cassel 1974), and therefore interventions are aimed at upholding or improving the substance of interaction within these alliances.

In 'Closed Doors', no one died; no one was divorced or abandoned; no one lost a limb; no one left home. But the family situation contained the potential for each of these. The couple had lost the mutual satisfaction and pleasure of their sexual life (Singer-Kaplan 1974). As well as the losses she listed throughout her marriage, the wife had most recently forfeited her job, her home, residence in a town she liked, and a social circle to which she could usefully contribute (Marris 1978; Weiss 1973). In terms of family life-cycle, she was soon to lose her two eldest children. The children in the family, too, had been removed from their familiar networks, and were thus deprived of their peers, school situation, and activities. It could be interpreted that they also lost their father through his rather gross underinvolvement (Haley 1976; Minuchin 1974; Minuchin, Rosman and Baker 1978). In any case, they did not seek contact with him any longer. Even if this father/husband had not lost contact with his children, he no longer held their esteem or appreciation. And it looked as if there was little left of his wife's trust or affection.

The losses on the part of the therapist in a case such as this are perhaps best conceived as missed opportunities. In the other case studies within this collection, the therapist gathers data (information, material, visible behaviour, and so on) from the patient and builds on it in the sense of

1   reframing the history of and circumstances around the problem, so

that what was beyond the comprehension and apparent control of the patient begins to make sense to him. He can see opportunities to influence some of the circumstances, or ways to resolve the problem itself;

2   detecting factors which show how the problem is created or maintained, in order to alter these so that the problem may be resolved;

3   discovering clues to what is important to the patient, in order to set goals, to describe 'what comes next'.

The data obtained in the sessions ought to assist the therapist in becoming acquainted with and appreciating the world picture of the patient. By failing to recognize the couple's situation as containing life events that were potentially dangerous (cf. Metze 1981; Simonton *et al.* 1978), the therapist was unable to discover how to treat or alter the family's response to them. She thereby lost her opportunity to assist.

The couple were not asked to elaborate the problem, in what ways it constituted a problem for them, what they hoped to gain from working with it at that point. It was here, just at the start, that the therapist missed a chance to begin working constructively. Too little information was obtained about ways the couple themselves attempted to solve the problem they presented.

The therapist should have taken into consideration the couple's previous attempts to seek help. Where a predicament or state persists over so many years, it may be supposed that there is some fault in the formulation of it as a problem which prevents solution. More strategically, she could have pointed out that, despite the seriousness of their condition, they were still able to achieve coitus at least once each month. It is a fact that some couples do not succeed to that extent. This sort of reframing might be further developed to build up the couple's abilities to satisfy each other sometimes; or to credit the couple in being able to overcome the stresses of the changes of recent years as well as this physical issue, in being partners to each other and parents to their children.

It is generally informative to meet a couple with their offspring, to get a picture of how the family functions as a whole. However, the presence of the children was not necessitated by the couple's presentation of their problem. The children's continued attendance in fact prevented formulation of a workable goal. And the therapist's repeated attempts to keep everyone involved and occupied merely excited their destructive behaviour.

The lessons to be learned from a story such as this are:

1   the importance of clear, concrete problem formulation and adherence to that formulation as a basis for therapeutic intervention

to be followed by

2   clear, simple, realistic goal formulation: what would this couple

accept as evidence of improvement in their circumstances? and this demands

3   taking seriously the problem presented and reframing it so as to appreciate its significance in the patients' life, and to assess their attempts to cope with it;
4   the necessity for vigilance and flexibility on the part of the therapist to alter their own behaviour in a way most advantageous to the outcome of therapy. In other words, to be able to

> match family members,
> challenge family behaviour or concepts,
> be friendly and supportive — or — provocative and contentious,
> be authoritarian — or — unobtrusive,
> repeat behaviour or statements,
> rapidly alter behaviour or stance,
> decide when and with whom to side,
> be grave — or — humorous.

This sort of flexibility is possible when the therapist evaluates the success or failure of approaches or techniques within each session, and discards those that are clearly ineffective — rather than persisting in an unhelpful attitude of unadulterated understanding.

This is important if the therapist is to avoid being stereotyped within the family system. Furthermore, it is one aspect of the authority that the therapist exercises both in challenging and in supporting changes in an individual or family system. For when a problem is allowed to deteriorate or to appear hopeless within therapy, the sorts of results that ensue are that the patient feels a failure, feels blamed by the expert, or 'learns' that professional assistance means problems getting worse.

This story shows how a therapist has been culpable in closing the little gap through which the family allowed her a look-in. Culpable, for the job of the therapist is to work towards opening — to widen the openings — rather than towards closing doors.

Notes

1   There is more than one possible explanation for the lack of information or anticipation in cases such as Elizabeth's. Given the particular practices amongst hospital personnel, it is equally likely that

(a)   Elizabeth's mother or father were told nothing about the findings of her father's examination
(b)   nothing was found
(c)   one or both parents were given an unclear message, or one too difficult for them to comprehend
(d)   the information was delivered under such circumstances (of stress, worry, distraction, etc.) that the receiver(s) were not able to hear or accommodate the information (Friedman et al. 1963; Janis 1973).

(e) one or both parents were informed, but chose not to share the information with the rest of the family

The book contains other examples where diagnoses and the ways in which they are delivered caused perhaps needless problems for the families of the patients. Hans' mother might have only received a diagnosis, but the interpretation she brought to my office was a prediction of Hans' imminent death. The issues at hand are basic:

(a) the ways in which diagnoses are conveyed to patients and their families
(b) how patients and their families receive and interpret the information conveyed.

The health professional cannot control the second, but is responsible for the first: the ways in which information is delivered to patients and their families. As more than one study in this collection suggest that the information delivery process causes problems in addition to the nature of the information which is conveyed, it can be inferred that much more attention should be afforded to communication between health professional and patient.

The range of literature in this area is vast. Of that mentioned in the bibliography at the end of this book, the interested reader is usefully referred to: Herter 1972; Kligerman 1972; Krant 1975; Kubler-Ross 1969; Maddison and Raphael 1972; Metze 1981; Saunders 1977; Stimson and Webb 1975; Webb and Stimson 1976.

2   The reader may be further referred to: Volkan 1966, 1970, 1971, 1972a, 1972b; Volkan and Showalter 1968.

3   In Denmark, patients are required to register with general practices within 10 kilometres of their place of residence. Irving and Berthe remained on the Laegernes Hus register, despite their move to another town. As Group 2 patients, or those who pay a portion of their medical fees privately, they are entitled to do this. Elenor, having moved to them from her father's home, had been registered with a practice there, and at the time of this visit, had most likely re-registered with a GP in her grandparents' new town.

8 Beyond the medical model

From the outset, this book has aimed to demonstrate applications of brief therapy with patients who presented a variety of somatic, psychiatric and less specific complaints. Integrating a psychosocial methodology into a general health practice admits of more than introducing new techniques. Agreement of certain values and principles precedes any incorporation of new ideals and practices into a service setting. These are expressed in the fundamental principles composed by the Laegernes Hus staff group (cf. Chapter 1, note 2).

Adopting a new orientation to concepts of illness and health, to the significance of symptoms and other bodily reactions, and to what constitutes the best treatment inevitably influences the day-to-day organization and execution of work. This influence extends both 'in' to the organization of the overall service, and 'out' into the community which receives and is informed by the service. The purpose of this chapter is to describe some of the changes which accompanied the integration of brief therapy as part of the clinic's treatment programme.

Brief therapy, as should be clear by now, is a psychotherapeutic model which seeks to promote beneficial change by alteration or substitution of behaviour patterns which perpetuate symptoms or problems for which the patient seeks remedy. The therapist seeks clarification about the symptom or problem, what part that problem plays in the patient's world, and what resources and limitations exist either to alleviate the conditions of the symptom or to solve the problem.

Once the application of this model to psychosocial treatment at Laegernes Hus began, all the primary health care professionals — the GPs, physiotherapist, nurses and district nurses, and midwives — adapted the model to their examination and interview procedures. Rather than fitting the patient into a regime of specialist categories, the therapist sought to discover what order of intervention would most quickly bring about positive change for the patient.

This shift in emphasis marks a modification of the treater–treated relationship, wherein the patient traditionally describes his symptoms, after which the treater deduces a diagnosis and prescribes treatment, which the patient is instructed to follow (Stimson and Webb 1975; Wadsworth 1976).

The brief therapy approach to problems and problem solving requires that the transactions and negotiations which take place between treater and treated assume a 'dialectic form. The treater *listens*[1] to the patient's formulation of his symptom. Rather than stopping at symptom description, the treater attempts to discover what meaning the discomfort has for the patient and his family (Friedman and Roseman 1974; Glass 1977; Hinkle and Wolff 1958; Lynch 1977; Metze 1981; Minuchin *et al.* 1978; Simonton and Simonton 1978). Symptoms are read, then, not only as conditions to cure, but as possible warnings of physical or emotional stress, as normal reactions to life events, or as analogic signals of disturbance in some aspect of the patient's system. Far from deferring use of his specialist knowledge by entering into such a dialogue with the patient, the treater employs his expertise to fuller effect by obtaining a richer picture of contributory factors. This enables him to identify where the patient's management of his condition has been counter-productive, and to devise a more expedient intervention or programme of treatment.

Such examinations may disclose cases where medical care is not the most advisable response. Once patients are encouraged to define their problem in their own terms rather than adhering to existing categories (as where Susanne requested admission to psychiatric care; or where Tora sought institutionalization as the best solution for her daughter; or where Lise and Michael maintained fertility charts for two years with neither follow-up from the prescribing doctor nor results for themselves), then the interface between treater and treated must become flexible and negotiable. The patient participates in his treatment in another respect than merely following treatment prescription. And then the form which intervention takes must more nearly match the patient's circumstances than match the expert's limited speciality (Laegernes Hus Gruppen 1980).

The notion that quality of service and care is not irrevocably linked to a hierarchy of expertise was an outgrowth of the theory from which family therapy sprang:

As part of the shift in premises about the nature of a problem and what to do about it, the helping professions must change. Traditionally a psychiatric problem was thought of as medical. Therefore it was correct that a medically trained psychiatrist be the primary authority and have the greatest status and salary. When the unit shifts from one person to two or more, the medical framework must be abandoned. Psychiatric problems become defined as social dilemmas . . . . It is not appropriate to think of a disease model, or an illness model, or to think of sickness and health.

As the unit of treatment changes and the problem is redefined, inevitably the professions must change . . . . A therapist is now often judged on merit — the success of his therapy — not on his professional background. Perhaps this is the most radical change introduced into the field by family therapy. (Haley 1971a, p. 284)

In the general practice at Laegernes Hus, redefining problems and rethinking the unit of treatment was paralleled by an interdisciplinary co-operation in assessing problem cases and in creating effective strategies to resolve them.

Conflicts between and within the caring professions tend to arise from differential models of care. Causation, objectives and working methods are conceptualized in specialist terms which frequently impede cross-fertilization rather than augment it. The sort of active participation which an interdisciplinary approach demands brings these conflicts to light. The efficacy of long-held assumptions and practices come under question when case analyses begin to examine the problems that professional intervention can produce, as well as the benefits.

Experience of integration at Laegernes Hus showed that, for the staff there to adopt a new orientation successfully, structural supports in the work setting were necessary. These uphold and facilitate an atmosphere of co-operation and learning, in which conflicts and differences that might arise from the progressive adaptation of new methods and techniques could be aired. Of the structural supports, twice weekly staff conferences were probably the most important, where the staff introduced cases, described encouraging or discouraging experiences with patients, colleagues and institutional contacts, shared knowledge about individuals or families, and contributed to planning. Weekly supervision sessions existed for those practising brief or family therapy, or those leading groups. Supervision and training sessions on aspects of psychosocial treatment were also available to all staff to support them in the advancement and continuity of the treatment programme.

A 'Statement on the Development of Interprofessional Education and Training for Members of Primary Health Care Teams' (1983), written by a British interdisciplinary committee representing health visitors, district nurses, general practitioners and social workers, included a set of goals which describes a basis for an approach to primary health care and recognizes the benefits of drawing upon all available resources:

1 Set objectives and provide care relevant to the whole person and that person's physical, psychological and social environment.
2 Make and execute plans for care which are flexible, pragmatic and realistic.
3 Co-operate with members of other professions on the basis of an awareness of their training and professional background . . . .
4 Seek help and support appropriately, from both his/her own hierarchy and from immediate colleagues in other disciplines; being conscious that seeking support is valid and responsible.
5 Recognise, and avoid, the risk that co-operation can become collusion of professionals against the client/patient.
6 Create a climate of mutual trust and respect between professionals and clients to assist the effective and improved delivery of care.
7 Demonstrate competence in shared decision making and evaluation.
8 Define additional shared learning needs. (p. 2)

150

The aptness of these principles can be seen in 'The Case of Caroline'.

Little Caroline did not develop as expected. At the age of three, she sat quietly in the corner while her twin sister Margaret talked and played with animation. Caroline was able to walk, but she rarely took any initiative to move. She often drooled, her nose tended to run, and she would cry if anyone tried to remove what she sat holding.

At the nursery school, Caroline was assigned a special support teacher (fritids pedagogue). He was meant to involve her in physical exercises and social activities with him and with the other children. After six months' efforts, neither he nor the nursery schoolteachers, or Caroline's parents could see any progress. Margaret thrived at the school. Now it was hard to believe that the girls were sisters, much less twins.

As consultant to the local education authority, Laegernes Hus' physiotherapist was requested to advise how, at least, Caroline's motor skills might be improved. She introduced Caroline's story at the staff conference and asked for ideas.

The health visitor was familiar with the household. It was her opinion that Caroline's mother was a capable woman. But the demands of running her own successful hairdressing salon were many. Even though her business hours were stated as 10.30 to 3, she could be seen working late more evenings than not. She was fortunate to have the assistance of a young housemaid who fetched the girls from nursery school most days. From what she had seen of the twins' elder brothers, 6 and 10, the health visitor thought that Caroline confounded them. In contrast to Margaret, her behaviour was irritating and incomprehensible. She generally cried when they tried to play with her, so they gradually came to leave her alone.

The psychotherapist asked if anyone knew the father. One of the doctors believed he had been pleased when the twins were girls. But little else was known about him, other than that he worked shifts at a factory. This had to mean that he was often at work at the times when his children were home.

Since no one could contribute any useful information about Caroline's developmental problem or potential, it was decided that the physiotherapist would observe Caroline in her normal routine at the nursery school, offer what advice she could to the teachers, and invite Caroline's support teacher to join the next conference.

The day after her visit to the nursery school, the physiotherapist reported the details of her visit over lunch. She had observed both Caroline and Margaret at play. She had demonstrated a few simple games that the teachers could use with Caroline. These were games which could also involve other children, so that Caroline would not be isolated while having special training. She had recommended to Freddie, Caroline's support teacher, that she might benefit from regular physical contact each day. She suggested he try to find out how she

151

would respond to his cuddling her for a quarter to half an hour each day, perhaps singing softly or humming to her as he did.

During a discussion prior to the conference to which Freddie was invited, Caroline's situation was reviewed. A strategy was devised based on what was known of the persons involved, the physiotherapist's assessment of Caroline's potential and limitations, and the prognosis of what could be achieved at the school. After six months, even with the aid of a special support teacher, the school had been unable to progress with her.

From past experiences, it seemed that introducing any new professionals into Caroline's resource network was not necessarily a helpful step. It was decided to activate those persons already comprising her network by explicitly assessing what their contribution and commitment could mean to Caroline's improvement. It was hoped that with such encouragement, key persons could step up their active involvement.

The ground was already laid for this strategy by the physiotherapist's intervention at the nursery school. The games she suggested built on their existing programme. They were fun exercises which could be used in small groups of nursery school pupils, and at the same time were purposeful. The teachers were able to afford extra attention to Caroline without increasing their work-load, or feeling they were neglecting their other pupils. Caroline was neither segregated from the others by her special needs, nor put in the role of a drag on the other children's enjoyment.

Since Freddie probably knew Caroline best of all the adults in her present world, he was viewed as the logical contact person between her and her parents. In fact, Freddie had been an unemployed kindergarten teacher who took the only opening available to him. He had little practical experience, and low status within the nursery school hierarchy. Neither his standing nor his self-esteem could have been enhanced by the six months he had worked with Caroline. It was precisely because of her lack of progress that the physiotherapist had been called in.

It was surmised that if the quality of his work were to improve, he would need some strategic encouragement. Further, it was proposed that if Caroline were to progress, some alteration must take place in her family's expectations and handling of her. To avoid introducing additional professional intrusion, Freddie's relation to Caroline was to be upheld as a source of insight and competence. It was decided to engage his co-operation as a catalyst to increased family involvement.

'You were right, Freddie,' the physiotherapist opened the discussion of Caroline's case, 'in your observation that Caroline functioned at an infantile level. It was your comment which gave me the idea that Caroline needed additional physical attention and non-demanding contact each day. How has that worked out?'

Freddie reported that Caroline seemed to benefit from this tactic. It also gave him more satisfaction than fruitlessly trying to get her to achieve something.

The health visitor then asked him if her impression of the household were accurate. Did he think Caroline's mother was overworked and that her father's shift schedule meant he lacked the opportunities to enjoy and keep in touch with his children.

'I hadn't thought of it so clearly, but you're right,' Freddie replied.

'Since you know Caroline so well, perhaps you'd be the best person to introduce some of these ideas about handling her in another way,' one of the women doctors offered helpfully. 'Sometimes parents of special children become so caught up with wearisome details, they miss points about their child that others can see clearly. The other teachers at the nursery school certainly didn't catch on to Caroline's needs. I can imagine that both Caroline and her parents would benefit from hearing what you have learned about the methods you have developed for working with her.'

The group nodded and looked at Freddie. Someone said that as a man, Freddie might be best able to communicate some clues to Caroline's father about the value of becoming more actively involved with the girls. He might, for instance, fetch them home from nursery school on the afternoons he was free. Freddie might describe in detail some of the games and the effects of the quiet time he spent with Caroline each day.

All at the conference agreed that each individual professionally engaged with anyone of Caroline's family should find ways to evaluate and encourage them. So when Caroline's mother came to Laegernes Hus for trouble with muscle tension, her doctor quite naturally prescribed physiotherapy.

During therapeutic massage, relaxed physically and mentally, Caroline's mother chatted about happenings in the town and about incidents in her business and her home, no doubt in the way her customers did at her salon. The physiotherapist chatted about Billund, and her work. She mentioned some readings she had encountered about child development, and she casually commented on her admiration of the family's desire to maintain places for both twins in the community, despite their differences. It wasn't an easy job trying to raise an under-developed child in today's busy and unsympathetic society. She informed Caroline's mother of some of the findings in her own practice, and shared what she knew of the new regime the teachers were beginning with Caroline at the nursery school.

Before the end of the month, Freddie had made a home visit. It is not unusual for special teachers to make contact with parents, but Freddie had been avoiding it. He finally felt he had something positive to say. He described how well Caroline responded to non-demanding care and affection. This had taught him a lot, and he wondered if the

153

family might not, too, discover other results if they adjusted their expectations to what Caroline could manage. He related the process he went through before he stopped comparing Caroline with Margaret. He finished with a casual discussion with Caroline's father. Freddie, in his ingenuous fashion, said how amazed he had been to see how important *time* seemed for Caroline: simply time for herself to receive affection, not be pressed, and to have the full attention of the persons she knew.

Freddie was able to continue learning from and with Caroline at the nursery school. The teachers there came to accept the age-differential concept in their expectations of the twins. The health visitor reported that both twins appeared to be benefiting from parental contact. On her last visit to the family, she found Margaret helping the boys set the table while Caroline sat snugly in her father's lap, where he was reading her a story.

About eight months after the strategic conference, the physiotherapist reported that on a recent call at the nursery school, she observed Caroline moving with perceptibly improved co-ordination, and taking more independent action. The teachers informed her that Caroline's social interaction was enriched and she played with the younger pupils better than before. There was even some discussion about preparing Caroline for primary school. The physiotherapist was asked her opinion on this plan. It was certainly in line with her parents' hopes for her to attend a normal school.

The doctor who recommended Freddie's first home visit to Caroline's parents found him in her surgery one day. After his examination, they chatted about Caroline. Freddie was still astounded and rather proud at Caroline's achievements over the past months. Much to his surprise, her father had begun to fetch the twins from nursery school occasionally, after his visit. This made him feel he had to continue his support of the man, and to report to the parents about his work with Caroline. The parental contacts, and the changes he saw made him take more seriously what could be accomplished through ordinary means — physical reassurance, acceptance, realistic expectations. It was a lesson he hoped he would never forget.

The case of Caroline illustrates the features outlined earlier:

1   *The importance of gathering information to put the problem into context.* Assessment of attempts to solve the problem uncovered resources and limitations in the circumstances. Increasing the number of personnel was not a solution in itself. Inappropriate deployment of such staff can serve to 'prove' the hopelessness of a situation. Moreover, an increase in the number of persons or agencies involved often leads to diffusion of responsibility and

accountability. Chances of effective action are reduced. This holds true whether in a small community or a metropolitan setting.

The most realistic action in these circumstances was therefore deemed to be to strengthen and invigorate the existing resources, at both institutional and familial levels. Explicit encouragement or confrontation were passed over as means of pursuing these aims in favour of a strategic approach.

2   *The primary aim of intervention was not to resolve all the difficulties presented but rather to alter the sequences or attempted solutions which perpetuated them.* There existed, in fact, no single intervention which would ensure Caroline's development, or even prevent continuation of her apparent standstill. The assumption which made the problem seem insuperable was that such a singular intervention might be found: treatment, or the right exercise programme, or the increased involvement of experts.

The approach conceived in the conference aimed to cultivate the social milieu or conditions which could foster the child's growth. Interventions reinforced the people in her network most likely to enrich their contacts with Caroline, and to co-operate in contributing to a common purpose — which could be seen to have results.

3   *The solution is not necessarily discovered in the specialist category from which help is sought.* The intervention was initiated by the nursery school staff's bid for the physiotherapist's consultation. The advice and exercises that were prescribed were very basic ones, suited to most young children. Caroline — and all the other pupils — certainly benefited from doing them. But in planning the strategy to combat Caroline's 'lack of development', non-medical factors were identified as instrumental to progress. Medical and non-medical personnel, professional helpers and family alike contributed to the problem-solving process.

4   *Co-operative participation in reformulating problems and in devising strategies.* All possible resources can be realistically engaged in constructing sensitive, competent, non-intrusive means of assistance and support. The story shows the usefulness of open communication, and the importance of interdisciplinary meetings, staff conferences and formal and informal discussion which facilitate creative adaptation of the model to everyday problems in the practice.

Perhaps it was inevitable that the original Laegernes Hus goals evolved so as to admit more active participation of the patients:

To work in order to make patients, ourselves and other professionals conscious of their own resources, and the possibilities to remain healthy. *[To maintain] an unconditional and continuous appreciation of where [the patient] is, in order to create opportunities for ourselves and [patients] to mark and make use of existing resources and possibilities.* And at the same time to treat illness.[2]

Human ecologists propose that the immediate social context in which the individual participates intervenes between objective and subjective stresses, and thus conditions the health outcome. They build their case on the findings of numerous surveys which examined the social forces suspected of contributing to maintenance and promotion of people's health. The research was carried out in both health-related and social science disciplines. The studies sought to discover how factors such as culture, change, environment, and personal and interpersonal properties related to susceptibility to physical illness.

The work at the Human Ecology Study Program at Cornell University and other investigations into the relationship between disturbance and adversity in the environment and the onset and form of psychiatric and physical illnesses report similar findings. *Personal variables*, such as psychological defences, past experiences, and cognitive processes, and *situational variables*, in the physical and social environment are proposed as the prime factors effecting (a) the individual's capability to adapt and (b) resultant differential vulnerability to illness (Gottlieb 1981; Hinkle and Wolff 1958; Hinkle 1974; Holmes and Rahe 1967; Meyer 1951; Rabkin and Struening 1976).

From empirical enquiries carried out in various industrial settings, the Survey Research Centre and the Research Center for Group Dynamics at the University of Michigan schematized four sets of variables whose interaction, they proposed, *determined* [sic] the health of their subjects (French and Kahn 1962; Gottlieb, ibid.):

1 properties of the objective social environment
2 characteristics of the psychological environment; together these reflect the individual's own perception and experience of the objective social environment
3 characteristics of the person: psychological states, physiological states, self identity
4 characteristics of the individual's behaviour: coping techniques and defensive styles expressed in the process of adjustment to the environment
(p. 15)

Gottlieb introduces Bloom's integration (1979) of existing material into a revised epidemiological framework. From his work on the relation between stressful life events and occurrence of illness, Bloom concluded that illness is induced by triggering or precipitating events in the individual's current environment, not necessarily by long-standing predispositions. Furthermore, that stressful life events and transitions appear to increase general vulnerability to disease, not susceptibility to specific diseases:

He then brings these two conclusions to bear in his revision of the traditional public health formulation of prevention, arguing that, while the accepted epidemiological model begins by identifying a specific disease and proceeds to pinpoint and eradicate its causes, his conclusions suggest that one should instead begin by identifying those life events with harmful *general* consequences and then seek to reduce or eradicate those consequences . . . Bloom maintains that . . . we should turn our efforts toward designing preventive interventions on behalf of populations experiencing those stressful life events known to generate adverse emotional outcomes . . . that social support offers one important avenue for neutralizing these consequences . . . It is [believed] particularly advisable to take this avenue when people face life events that entail or threaten the loss of significant social ties. Events involving potentially great social losses include divorce and separation . . . death of a social intimate, job loss, retirement, and geographic moves. Other events requiring reorientation to or rearrangement of the social environment include first-time parenthood . . . school and college entrance, and job changes. The more general implication of Bloom's 'new paradigm' for primary intervention is that social support is a key resource for health promotion because of its 'generally' salutary but unspecifiable effect on health. (Gottlieb 1981, pp. 27–28)

These works consistently illuminate the significance of the individual's relation to his social milieu. If the psychosocial practitioner accepts that psychological characteristics (such as self-esteem, perception of self and social environment, coping mechanisms, and ability to learn from and integrate previous experience) assist the individual to cope with the effects of life events, and that the social network constitutes a key factor both in mediating pressures and in providing resources to enable the individual to survive his environment, then his practice must reflect this belief by attending to those factors in the patient's life. A request for treatment or assistance creates the opportunity to reinforce the qualities which facilitate the patient's participation in (that is, use of and contribution to) the range of his social network.

To argue this point with a pragmatic example, institutionalization has become an alternative to the way in which patients or their professional carers manage physical, social or psychiatric difficulties. As such, institutionalization has been regularly regarded as more intensive treatment, or a solution to difficult cases. At Laegernes Hus, long-term institutionalization has been viewed in most cases as a way of worsening the problem or prolonging it. The purpose of the sorts of interventions described in this book was to bring about change in the client's situation so that institutionalization or more intense, specialized assistance or treatment was not necessary. The aim was not to change the patient, but to assist the patient to change his relationship to his environment and his way of dealing with the persons in it. This meant working to:

- recognize opportunities in human tribulation
- learn to formulate aims and aspirations and to activate the means within self and environment to achieve them
- equip and encourage individuals to meet challenges of daily life, and to confront and manage crises which may occur

The side-effects of this work lie outside the realms of scientific measure. The case studies in this volume testify that they are not meaningless to it (for example, cf. Cousins 1981; Lynch 1977). It is clear — in the accounts of some patients, in the complaints of patient consumer groups, in the medical sociology literature — that professional answers do not match all problems presented to the professional care sector.

We argue that those working with the physiological, emotional and social problems of others must be allowed — encouraged — to seek new replies and new resolutions, and to discover and use the opportunities encountered *in* patients and *for* them.

Notes

1   Listening is noted here as a key faculty in applying the brief therapy or any other psychosocial model to care. It is a seriously underrated activity amongst all helping professionals. The statement is but one example of the sort of data medical sociologists repeatedly collect and present as patients' commentaries on the nature of treater–treated interaction.

> When I'm walking in my doctor's, he just finds out first of all if I've got the children with me, which I've come for, or whether I've come for myself, and once he's found that out he's writing the name and address on the prescription while I'm talking to him. He doesn't know what I want, you know. I say, 'One of these days' — I went into him and said, 'One of these days you'll write the prescription out before I even tell you what's wrong!' You know he's in the middle of doing it as I'm talking to him, you know. (Stimson and Webb 1975, p. 1)

2   Translated statement of goal clarification from the personnel group to the researchers ('we' and 'our' once again expresses the staff voice rather than that of the authors):

> We wanted to use the words 'to create opportunities' to emphasize that this is the most we hope to achieve on the first meeting. The outcomes at the end of a meeting are a product of the process which takes place between us and the other.
>
> The words 'ourselves and others' are used instead of words such as 'man', 'men', 'the individual' to emphasize the fact that these meetings take place between two or more persons.
>
> We have chosen to divide our goal setting into three sections:
>
> (a) The act of developing awareness of resources and possibilities to become and stay healthy, is mentioned first. It is considered by us the foundation of our work — in individual situations and with others. It serves as a premise for the preventative work, and for the other sections of the goal setting.
> (b) We acknowledge the necessity of continuing to treat illness.
> (c) At the same time, we strive to familiarize ourselves with the illness-provoking factors in the local society.

This ideal of enabling patients to anticipate life events pervades the broad aims for specific 'untraditional' activities in the health programme at Laegernes Hus (translated from the Danish):

Family Preparation Groups

Acknowledging that life begins before birth and that a pregnancy brings about changes in a family's experiences, we want to use the special event which expecting and giving birth to a child constitutes, to lay the foundation for the processes which follow a birth amongst the involved persons. We regard this as a worthwhile aim because it stimulates in the parents-to-be awareness and skills which can improve the possibilities of family members to meet their own needs and the needs of each other.

Well-baby Examinations

We acknowledge that interaction between children and parents determines the child's development. In these examinations, which take place at regular intervals until the child reaches the age of 5 years, we aim to promote and support the parents in meeting their children's needs, notably, by engendering contact, confidence and trust, and safety and security; in development as individuals and in interaction with others; in learning body awareness, personal imagination, and ways for tackling risk situations; and in order to foster mutual responsibility between parent and child. It is also the aim of these examinations to detect and treat abnormality and disease in the child.

Medical Treatment of Children under 6 Years Old

Examinations when children are brought for treatment outside the structure of well-baby examinations are of a different nature, and hence have different goals.

We want to lay the foundations for the processes which contribute to the child's development — on its own terms — when illness or social events have created disorder or imbalance in the family system. [This aim can be seen brought into play in the case of Caroline, whose impairment hindered her development.]

The School Doctor Function

We want to enlarge the pupils' understanding of their own and others' worth through developing responsible values and behaviour for their own health.

Brief Therapy Treatment

Assuming there are connections between social events, man's inner balance, his relation to other persons, and illnesses which occur, we want to help the individual to solve the problems he encounters on his own terms and in the best way possible for him.

Group Work for Patients with Emotional, Social or Somatic Difficulties

We aim to give individuals who want to change their circumstances the possibility, in a group setting with persons of similar complaints, to

> exchange experiences
> become more aware of the particulars of their problem
> use each other's resources
> take responsibility for themselves

so that each group member can discover new opportunities within himself and his network.

Bibliography

Adams, Roger and Hill, Gordon (1983), 'The labours of Hercules: some good reasons why social workers should not try to be different, and practice family therapy', *Journal of Family Therapy*, 5, (1), 71–80.

Adler, Gerald *et al.* (1975), 'Approaches to intervention with dying patients and their families: a case discussion' in Bernard Schoenberg *et al.* (eds), *Bereavement: Its Psychosocial Aspects*, Columbia University Press, 281–93.

Andolfi, Maurice (1979), *Family Therapy: An Interactional Approach*, Plenum Press, New York.

Argyris, Chris (1970), *Intervention Theory and Method: A Behavioural Science View*, Addison Wesley, Mass.

Argyris, Chris (1974), *Theory in Practice: Increasing Professional Effectiveness*, Jossey-Bass, New York.

Beer, Stafford (1975), *Platform for Change*, John Wiley, London.

Beitman, B.D. *et al.* (1982), 'Steps toward patient acknowledgment of psychosocial factors', *Journal of Family Therapy*, 15, (6), 1119–26.

Billis, David (1981), 'At risk of prevention', *Journal of Social Policy*, 10, (3), 367–79.

Bloch, Donald A. (1982), 'Thirteen years: an editor's valedictory', *Family Process*, 21, (4), December 1982, 383–9.

Bloom, B.L. (1979), 'Prevention of mental disorders: recent advances in theory and practice', *Community Mental Health Journal*, 15, 179–91.

Bohannan, Paul (1971), 'The six stations of divorce' in Paul Bohannan (ed.), *Divorce and After: an Analysis of the Emotional and Social Problems of Divorce*, Doubleday Anchor Books, 33–62.

Brockway, Barbara (1978), 'Behavioural medicine in family practice: a unifying approach for the assessment and treatment of psychosocial problems', *Journal of Family Therapy*, 6, (3), 545–52.

Byrnes, Patrick and Long, Barrie (1976), *Doctors Talking to Patients*, DHSS, Her Majesty's Stationery Office, London.

Caplan, G. (1974), 'Support systems' in G. Caplan (ed.), *Support Systems and Community Mental Health*, Basic Books, New York.

Carter, E.A. and McGoldrick (eds) (1980), *The Family Life Cycle: a Framework for Family Therapy*, Gardner Press, New York.

Cassel, J. (1974), 'Psychological processes and "stress": theoretical formulations', *International Journal of Health Services*, 4, 471—82.

Cassem, Ned H. (1975), 'Bereavement as indispensable for growth' in Bernard Schoenberg *et al.* (eds), *Bereavement: Its Psychosocial Aspects*, Columbia University Press, New York, 9—17.

Cath, Stanley H. (1965), 'Some dynamics of the middle and later years' in Howard J. Parad (ed.), *Crisis Intervention: Selected Readings*, Family Service Association of America, New York, 174—90.

Cobb, S. (1979), 'Social support and health through the life course' in M.W. Riley (ed.), *Aging from Birth to Death*, Westview Press, Boulder, Colorado.

Council for the Education and Training of Health Visitors *et al.* (approx. 1983), 'Statement on the development of interprofessional education and training for members of primary health care teams', unpublished statement, England.

Cousins, Norman (1981), *Anatomy of an Illness as Perceived by the Patient*, Bantam Books, New York.

Cullberg, Johan (1975), *Kris och Utveckling*, Natur och Kultur, Stockholm.

Cutter, Fred (1974), *Coming to Terms with Death*, Nelson-Hall Company Publisher, Chicago.

De Bono, Edward (1973), *PO: Beyond Yes and No*, Penguin Books, Harmondsworth.

Dimatteo, M. Robin and Hays, Ron (1981), 'Social support and serious illness' in Benjamin H. Gottlieb (ed.), *Social Networks and Social Support*, Sage Publications, Beverly Hills.

Dohrenwend, B.S. and Dohrenwend, B.P. (1978), 'Some issues in research on stressful life events', *Journal of Nervous and Mental Disease*, 166, 7—15.

Donzelot, Jacques (1979), *The Policing of Families*, Pantheon Books, New York.

Dyne, Geoffrey (ed.) (1981), *Bereavement Visiting*, King Edward's Hospital Fund for London.

Eckenrode, John and Gore, Susan (1981), 'Stressful events and social supports: the significance of context' in Benjamin H. Gottlieb (ed.), *Social Networks and Social Support*, Sage Publications, Beverly Hills.

Eisdorfer, C. and Lawton, M.P. (eds) (1973), *The Psychology of Adult Development and Aging*, American Psychological Association, Washington, DC.

Engel, G.L. (1970), 'Sudden death and the medical model in psychiatry', *Canadian Psychiatric Association Journal*, 15, 527—38.

Erikson, Erik H. (1950), *Childhood and Society*, Norton, New York.

Fisch, Richard, Weakland, J. and Segal, L. (1982), *The Tactics of Change*, Jossey-Bass Publishers, San Francisco.

Forster, E.M. (1974), *Aspects of the Novel*, Penguin Books, Harmondsworth.

Foucault, Michel (1973), *The Birth of the Clinic*, Tavistock Publications, London.

Francke, Linda Bird (1983), *Growing Up Divorced*, Linden Press, New York.

Frankl, Victor (1959), *Man's Search for Meaning*, Pocket Books/Simon and Schuster, New York.

French, J.R.P. jr and Kahn, R.L. (1962), 'A programmatic approach to studying the industrial environment and mental health', *Journal of Social Issues*, 18, 1—47.

French, J.R.P. jr (1974), 'Person-role fit' in A. McLean (ed.), *Occupational Stress*, Charles C. Thomas, Springfield, Illinois.

Friedman, Alfred S. *et al.* (1965), *Psychotherapy for the Whole Family*, Springer Publishing Co. Inc., New York.

Friedman, S.B., Chodoft, D., Mason, J.W. and Hamburg, D.A. (1963), 'Behavioural observations on parents anticipating the death of a child', *Pediatrics*, 32, 610—25.

Friedman, S.B. *et al.* (1967), 'Care of the family of the child with cancer', *Pediatrics*, 40, 498.

Friedman, W. *et al.* (1978a), 'Group therapy in family medicine: part 1', *Journal of Family Practice*, 6, (5), 1015—18.

Friedman, W. *et al.* (1978b), 'Group therapy in family medicine: part 2: establishing the group', *Journal of Family Practice*, 6, (6), 1243—47.

Friedman, W. *et al.* (1978c), 'Group therapy in family medicine: part 3: starting the group', *Journal of Family Practice*, 7, (2), 317—20.

Friedman, W. *et al.* (1978d), 'Group therapy in family medicine: part 4: a case report', *Journal of Family Practice*, 7, (3), 501—3.

Friedman, W. and Roseman (1974), *Type A Behaviour and Your Heart*, Alfred A. Knopf Inc., New York.

Gerber, Irwin *et al.* (1975), 'Brief therapy to the aged bereaved' in Bernard Schoenberg *et al.* (eds), *Bereavement: its Psychosocial Aspects*, Columbia University Press, New York, 310—33.

Glass, D.C. (1977), *Behaviour Patterns, Stress and Coronary Disease*, Lawrence Erlbaum Associates, New Jersey.

Glasser, Paul H. *et al.* (1970), *Families in Crisis*, Harper and Row, New York.

Glasser, William (1965), *Reality Therapy*, Harper and Row, New York.

Goldstine, Daniel (1983), 'Divorce is not ending', *The New York Times Book Review*, 24 July, 9, 24.

Gottlieb, Benjamin H. (1981) (ed.), *Social Networks and Social Support*, Sage Publications, Beverly Hills.

Greenwald, Harold (1973), *Direct Decision Therapy*, Edits, San Diego, California.

Grinder, John and Bandler, Richard (1975), *The Structure of Magic Vol. I*, Science and Behaviour Books Inc.

Grof, Stanislav *et al.* (1975), *Realms of the Human Unconscious*, Viking Press Inc., New York.

Haley, Jay (1963), *Strategies of Psychotherapy*, Grune and Stratton, New York.

Haley, Jay (1967), *Techniques of Family Therapy*, Basic Books, New York.

Haley, Jay (1971a), *Changing Families: a Family Therapy Reader*, Grune and Stratton, New York.

Haley, Jay (1971b), *The Power Tactics of Jesus Christ and Other Essays*, Avon Books, New York.

Haley, Jay (1973), *Uncommon Therapy*, W.W. Norton and Company, Inc., New York.

Haley, Jay (1976), *Problem-Solving Therapy*, Jossey-Bass Inc., San Francisco.

Haley, Jay (1980), *Leaving Home*, McGraw-Hill Book Company, New York.

Henry, Jules (1972), *Pathways to Madness*, Random House, New York.

Henry, Jules (1973), 'Personality and aging — with special reference to hospitals for the aged poor' in Jules Henry, *On Sham, Vulnerability and Other Forms of Self Destruction*, Random House, New York, 16—39.

Herr, John and Weakland, John (1979), *Counselling Elders and their Families*, Springer, New York.

Herter, Frederic P. (1972), 'A surgeon looks at terminal illness' in Bernard Schoenberg *et al.* (eds), *Psychosocial Aspects of Terminal Care*, Columbia University Press, New York, 79—87.

Hill, Michael (1977), *Handbook for Better Meetings*, Bloch Petrella Associates, New Jersey.

Hinkle, L.E. jr (1974), 'The effects of exposure to culture change, social change and changes in interpersonal relationships on health' in B.S. Dohrenwend and B.P. Dohrenwend (eds), *Stressful Life Events*, John Wiley, New York.

Hinkle, L.E. jr and Wolff, H.G. (1958), 'Ecological investigations of the relations between illness, life experiences and the social environment', *Annals of International Medicine*, 49, 1373—88.

Hirsch, Barton J. (1981), 'Social networks and the coping process: creating personal communities' in Benjamin H. Gottlieb (ed.), *Social Networks and Social Support*, Sage Publications, Beverly Hills.

Hoffman, Lynn (1981), *Foundations of Family Therapy*, Basic Books, New York.

Hollingsworth, C.E. *et al.* (1977), 'The sudden death' in *The Family in Mourning*, Grune and Stratton, New York.

Holmes, T.H. and Rahe, R.H. (1967), 'The social readjustment rating scale', *Journal of Psychosomatic Research*, 11, 213–18.

Huygen, F.J.A. (1982), *Family Medicine*, Brunner/Mazel, New York.

Janis, I.L. (1958), *Psychological Stress*, John Wiley, New York.

Janis, I.L. (1973), *Psychological Stress: Psychoanalytic and Behavioural Studies of Surgical Patients*, Chapman and Hall, London.

Jordan, William (1981), 'Family therapy — an outsider's view', *Journal of Family Therapy*, 3, 269–80.

Katz, Alfred H. and Bender, Eugene (1976), *The Strength in Us : Self Help Groups in the Modern World*, New Viewpoints, New York.

Keleman, Stanley (1974), *Living Your Dying*, Random House, New York.

Kennedy, Ian (1983), *The Unmasking of Medicine*, Paladin, London.

Kleinman, Arthur (1980), *Patients and Healers in the Context of Culture*, University of California Press, London.

Kligerman, Morton M. (1972), 'A radiotherapist's view of the management of the cancer patient' in Bernard Schoenberg *et al.* (eds), *Psychosocial Aspects of Terminal Care*, Columbia University Press, New York, 101–5.

Krant, M.J. (1975), 'The health professionals' in Bernard Schoenberg *et al.* (eds), *Bereavement: Its Psychosocial Aspects*, Columbia University Press, New York, 217–25.

Krantzler, Mel (1975), *Creative Divorce*, The New American Library, New York.

Kubler-Ross, E. (1969), *On Death and Dying*, Macmillan Publishing Co., New York.

Kubler-Ross, E. (1978), *To Live Until We Say Goodbye*, Prentice Hall, Englewood Cliffs, New Jersey.

Laegehusgruppen I Billund (1980), *Hvordan Aendres Behandlerrollen*, Laefeforeningens Forlag, Copenhagen.

Laing, R.D. *et al.* (1970), *Sanity, Madness and the Family*, Penguin Books, Harmondsworth.

Lakein, Alan (1974), *How to Get Control of your Time and your Life*, Signet Books, New York.

Lasch, Christopher (1979), *Haven in a Heartless World*, Basic Books, New York.

Laurie, Peter (1974), *Meet your Friendly Social System*, Arrow, London.

Leboyer, Frederick (1976), *Fødsel Uden Vold*, Gyldendal, Copenhagen, *[Pour une Naissance sans Violence]*.

Leboyer, Frederick (1978), *Kaerlige Haender, Shantala*, Borgen, Copenhagen, *[Un Art Traditionnel, le Massage des Enfants]*.

Levinson, Daniel J. *et al.* (1978), *The Seasons of a Man's Life*, Knopf, New York.

Lewis, Jerry M. *et al.* (1976), *No Single Thread*, Brunner/Mazel, New York.

Lind, John, *et al.* (1981), *Musik I Livets Borjan*, Akademilitteratur AB, Stockholm.

Lindemann, E. (1944), 'Symptomology and management of acute grief', *American Journal of Psychiatry*, 101, 141 ff.

Lyall, Alan and Machon, Mary (1975), 'Professional roles in thanatology' in Bernard Schoenberg *et al.* (eds), *Bereavement: Its Psychosocial Aspects*, Columbia University Press, New York, 226–31.

Lynch, James L. (1977), *The Broken Heart*, Basic Books, New York.

Madanes, Cloe (1981), *Strategic Family Therapy*, Jossey-Bass, San Francisco.

Maddison, D. and Raphael, B. (1972), 'The family of the dying patient' in Bernard Schoenberg *et al.* (eds), *Psychosocial Aspects of Terminal Care*, Columbia University Press, New York, 185–200.

Maddison, D. and Raphael, B. (1975), 'Conjugal bereavement and the social network' in Bernard Schoenberg *et al.* (eds), *Bereavement: Its Psychosocial Aspects*, Columbia University Press, New York, 26–40.

Manocchio, A.J. *et al.* (1979), *Terapeutens Rolle I Samfundet*, Borgens Forlag, Copenhagen.

Manocchio, A.J. (1981), 'Therapeutic intervention with the dying patient and the family' in Pegg, P. and Metze, E. (eds), *Death and Dying: a Quality of Life*, Pitman, London, 111–24.

Marenker, Marshall (1976), 'The family in medicine', *Proceedings of Royal Society of Medicine*, 69, 115–24.

Marris, Peter (1978), *Loss and Change*, Routledge and Kegan Paul, London.

Maslow, Abraham (1976), *The Farther Reaches of Human Nature*, Penguin, New York.

Mauss, Marcel (1954), *The Gift: Forms and Function of Exchange in Archaic Societies*, Cohen and West, London.

Mechanic, D. (1972), 'Social psychological factors affecting the presentation of bodily complaints', *New England Journal of Medicine*, 286, 1132–9.

Metze, Erno (1981), 'The coronary patient – living with the possibility of sudden death' in Pegg, P. and Metze, E. (eds), *Death and Dying: a Quality of Life*, Pitman, London.

Meyer, Adolf (1951), 'The life chart and the obligation of specifying positive data in psychopathology' in E.E. Winters (ed.), *The Collected Papers of Adolf Meyer, Vol. III, Medical Teaching*, Johns Hopkins Press, Baltimore.

Miller, Lovick C. (1965), 'Short term therapy with adolescents' in Howard J. Parad (ed.), *Crisis Intervention: Selected Readings*, Family Service Association of America, New York, 157–66.

Minuchin, Salvador (1974), *Families and Family Therapy*, Tavistock Publications, London.

Minuchin, Salvador and Barcai, A. (1972), 'Therapeutically induced family crisis' in C. Sager and H. Singer-Kaplan (eds), *Progress in Group and Family Therapy*, Brunnel/Mazel, New York, 322—8.

Minuchin, Salvador and Fishman, H. Charles (1981), *Family Therapy Techniques*, Harvard University Press, Cambridge, Massachusetts.

Minuchin, Salvador, Rosman, Bernice and Baker, Lester (1978), *Psychosomatic Families*, Harvard University Press, Cambridge, Massachusetts.

Montalvo, Braulio and Haley, Jay (1981), 'In defense of child therapy' in Jay Haley (ed.), *Reflections on Therapy and Other Essays*, The Family Therapy Institute, Washington, DC, 133—50.

Oberg, Bente and Oberg, Gunnar (1978), *Nu Går Jag*, W and W, Stockholm.

O'Connor, John J. (1983), 'Why can't I get hives: brief strategic therapy with an obsessional child', *Family Process*, 22, June, 201—9.

Odent, Michel (1981), *Bedre Fødsel, Bedre Liv*, Borgen, Copenhagen, *[Bien Naître]*.

Palazzoli, M. *et al.* (1978), *Paradox and Counter Paradox*, Jason Aronson, New York.

Parkes, Colin Murray (1972), *Bereavement*, Penguin Books, Harmondsworth.

Parkes, Colin Murray (1975), 'Unexpected and untimely bereavement: a statistical study of young Boston widows and widowers' in Bernard Schoenberg *et al.* (eds), *Bereavement: Its Psychosocial Aspects*, Columbia University Press, New York, 119—38.

Parkes, Colin Murray (1976), 'The broken heart' in Edwin S. Schneidman (ed.), *Death: Current Perspectives*, Mayfield, Palo Alto, 333—47.

Parkes, Colin Murray (1981), 'Sudden death and its impact on the family', in P. Pegg and E. Metze (eds), *Death and Dying: a Quality of Life*, Pitman, London, 19—34.

Parsons, Talcott (1967), 'Illness and the role of the physician: a sociological perspective' in Kluckhohn and Murray (eds), *Personality: In Nature, Society and Culture*, Alfred A. Knopf, New York.

Pegg, P.F. and Metze, E. (1981) (eds), *Death and Dying: a Quality of Life*, Pitman, London.

Pegg, P.F. and Pegg, M. (1975), 'Building on strengths', *New Psychiatry*, 14 August.

Pinker, R. (1971), *Social Theory and Social Policy*, Heinemann Educational Books, London.

Pressey, Sidney L. and Kuhlen, Raymond (1957), *Psychological Development through the Life Span*, Harper and Brothers, New York.

Rabkin, J.G. and Struening, E.L. (1978), 'Life events, stress and illness', *Science*, 194, 1013—20.

Rapoport, Lydia (1965), 'The state of crisis: some theoretical considerations' in Howard J. Parad (ed.), *Crisis Intervention: Selected Readings*, Family Service Association of America, New York.

Rosenblatt, P.C. (1981), 'Grief in cross cultural and historical perspective' in P.F. Pegg and E. Metze (eds), *Death and Dying: a Quality of Life*, Pitman, London, 11—18.

Rothberg, Barbara (1983), 'Joint custody: parental problems and satisfactions', *Family Process*, 22, 43—52.

Ruesch, Jurgen (1973), *Therapeutic Communication*, W.W. Norton and Co., New York.

Satir, Virginia (1967), *Conjoint Family Therapy*, Science and Behaviour Books, Palo Alto.

Satir, Virginia (1972), *Peoplemaking*, Science and Behaviour Books, Palo Alto.

Saunders, Cicely (1972), 'A therapeutic community: St Christopher's Hospice' in Bernard Schoenberg *et al.* (eds), *Psychosocial Aspects of Terminal Care*, Columbia University Press, New York, 275—89.

Saunders, Cicely (1977), 'Dying they live: St Christopher's Hospice' in Herman Feifel (ed.), *New Meanings of Life*, McGraw-Hill, New York, 153—79.

Scheff, Thomas J. (1966), *Being Mentally Ill*, Aldine, Chicago.

Schein, Edgar (1969), *Process Consultation: Its Role in Organisation Development*, Addison Wesley, Massachusetts.

Schneider, John (1981), 'Growth from bereavement' in P.F. Pegg and E. Metze (eds), *Death and Dying: a Quality of Life*, Pitman, London, 35—57.

Schneidman, Edwin S. (1976), *Death: Current Perspectives*, Mayfield, Palo Alto.

Schoenberg, Bernard *et al.* (eds) (1970), *Loss and Grief*, Columbia University Press, New York.

Sheehy, Gail (1974), *Passages*, E.P. Dutton, New York.

Sheehy, Gail (1982), *Pathfinders*, Bantam Books, New York.

Silverman, Phyllis R. (1976), 'The widow-to-widow program: an experiment in preventive intervention' in Edwin S. Schneidman (ed.), *Death: Current Perspectives*, Mayfield, Palo Alto, 356—63.

Simonton and Simonton *et al.* (eds) (1978), *Getting Well Again*, J.P. Tarcher, Los Angeles.

Singer-Kaplan, Helen (1974), *The New Sex Therapy: Active Treatment of Sexual Dysfunctions*, Brunner/Mazel, New York.

Sluzki, Carlos E. (1983), 'Process, structure and world views: towards an integrated view of systemic models in family therapy', *Family Process*, 22, (4), 469—76.

Sohl and Carr (eds) (1976), *Games Zen Masters Play*, New American Library, New York.

Sontag, Susan (1979), *Illness as Metaphor*, Allen Lane, London.

Speck, R. and Attneave, C. (1973), *Family Networks*, Pantheon Books, New York.

Stimson, G. and Webb, B. (1975), *Going to See the Doctor: the Consultation Process in General Practice*, Routledge and Kegan Paul, London.

Thornes, Barbara *et al.* (1979), *Who Divorces?*, Routledge and Kegan Paul, London.

Tolsdorf, C.C. (1976), 'Social networks, support and coping: an exploratory study', *Family Process*, 15, 407–17.

Tolstoy, L.N. (1971), *Anna Karenina*, Penguin, Harmondsworth.

Van Gennep, Arnold (1960) [1908], *The Rites of Passage*, University of Chicago Press, Chicago, Illinois.

Verny, Thomas *et al.* (1981), *Det Ufødte Barns Hemmelige Liv*, Borgen, Copenhagen, *[The Secret Life of the Unborn Child]*.

Volkan, V.D. (1966), 'Normal and pathological grief reactions — a guide for the family physician', *Virginia Medical Monthly*, 93, 651 ff.

Volkan, V.D. (1970), 'Typical findings in pathological grief', *Psychiatric Quarterly*, 44, 231 ff.

Volkan, V.D. (1971), 'A study of a patient's re-grief work through dreams, psychological tests and psychoanalysis', *Psychiatric Quarterly*, 45, 255 ff.

Volkan, V.D. (1972a), 'The linking objects of pathological mourners', *Archives of General Psychiatry*, 27, 215 ff.

Volkan, V.D. (1972b), 'The recognition and prevention of pathological grief', *Virginia Medical Monthly*, 99, 535 ff.

Volkan, V.D. (1975), '"Re-grief" therapy' in Bernard Schoenberg *et al.* (eds), *Bereavement: Its Psychosocial Aspects*, Columbia University Press, New York, 334–50.

Volkan, V.D. and Showalter, C.R. (1968), 'Known object loss, disturbance in reality testing, and "re-grief" work as a method of brief psychotherapy', *Psychiatric Quarterly*, 42, 358 ff.

Volkan, V.D. *et al.* (1975), 'Re-grief therapy and the function of the linking object as a way to stimulate emotionality' in P. Olsen (ed.), *Emotional Flooding*, Human Science Press, New York.

Wadsworth, Michael (1976), 'Studies of doctor–patient communication' in Michael Wadsworth and David Robinson (eds), *Studies in Everyday Medical Life*, Martin Robertson, London, 3–12.

Wallman, Sandra *et al.* (1980), 'Ethnography by proxy: strategies for research in the inner city', *Ethnos*, 1, 5–38.

Walsh, Froma (1982), *Normal Family Processes*, The Guilford Press, New York.

Watzlawick, Paul (1976), *How Real is Real?*, Random House, New York.

Watzlawick, Paul (1978), *The Language of Change*, Basic Books, New York.

Watzlawick, Paul, Weakland, John and Fisch, Richard (1974), *Change: Problem Formulation and Problem Resolution*, W.W. Norton and Co., New York.

Watzlawick, Paul *et al.* (1977), *The Interactional View*, W.W. Norton and Co., New York.

Weakland, John *et al.* (1974), 'Brief therapy: focused problem resolution', *Family Process*, 13, (2), 141–68.

Webb, B. and Stimson, G. (1976), 'People's accounts of medical encounters' in Michael Wadsworth and David Robinson (eds), *Studies in Everyday Medical Life*, Martin Robertson, London, 108–22.

Weeks, Gerald and l'Abate, Luciano (1982), *Paradoxical Psychotherapy: Theory and Practice with Individuals, Couples and Families*, Brunner/Mazel, New York.

Weiss, Robert S. (1973), *Loneliness*, The MIT Press.

Weiss, Robert S. (1975), *Marital Separation*, Basic Books, New York.

Wellman, Barry (1981), 'Applying network analysis to the study of support' in Benjamin H. Gottlieb (ed.), *Social Networks and Social Support*, Sage Publications, Beverly Hills.

Wiener, Alfred *et al.* (1975), 'The process and phenomenology of bereavement' in Bernard Schoenberg *et al.* (eds), *Bereavement: its Psychosocial Aspects*, Columbia University Press, New York, 53–65.

Zorn, Fritz (1982), *Mars*, Pan Books, London.

Zuk, Gerald H. (1972), 'The side-taking function in family therapy' in Clifford Sager and Helen Singer-Kaplan (eds), *Progress in Group and Family Therapy*, Brunner/Mazel, New York, 376–84.

Index